SEA

Reef

N

BOWEN

Whitsunday

N. Molle I.

W. Molle I.

Hayman I.
Hook I.

Whitsunday I.

Sth Molle

Dent I.

PROSERPINE

Long I.

Lindeman I.

Shaw I.

Cumberland Islands

Repulse Bay

Passage

Sir James Smith
Group

Carlisle I.

N

Brampton I.

Keswick I.
St Bees I.

MACKAY

0   MILES

Saumarez
Reef

Hinchbrook I.

acirda Pt

Palm Is

Halifax Bay

Magnetic I.

C. Cleveland

Gloucester I.

SEE INSET

Swain Reefs

Beverley Group

Cumberland
Is

Percy Is

Flat Is

Long I.

Northumberland Is

Shoalwater Bay

Townshend I.

OWNSVILLE

BOWEN

PROSERPINE

MACKAY

Capricorn
Group

North
Reef

Heron I.

Nor'West I.

Lady
Musgrave I.

Curtis I.

Lady Elliot I.

Bunker Group

Sandy Cape

ROCKHAMPTON

GLADSTONE

Hervey
Bay

BUNDABERG

MARYBOROUGH

Q U E E N S L A N D

TROPIC OF CAPRICORN

MILES

0   50   100   150   200   250   300

RAILWAYS ———

THE GREAT BARRIER REEF

Books by W. J. Dakin

PECTEN (1909)

BUCCINUM (1912)

PEARLS (1913)

THE ELEMENTS OF ANIMAL BIOLOGY (1918)

ELEMENTS OF GENERAL ZOOLOGY (1927)

WHALEMEN ADVENTURERS (1934)

THE ART OF CAMOUFLAGE (1941)

AUSTRALIAN SEASHORES (1952)
(with Isobel Bennett and Elizabeth Pope)

The Great Barrier Reef

AND SOME MENTION OF OTHER AUSTRALIAN CORAL REEFS

by the late
WILLIAM J. DAKIN, D.Sc.
Emeritus Professor of Zoology, University of Sydney

revised by
ISOBEL BENNETT, M.Sc.
Department of Zoology, University of Sydney

Ure Smith • Sydney
in association with
THE AUSTRALIAN NATIONAL TRAVEL ASSOCIATION

First published 1950; 2nd impression 1953; reprinted 1955
This second edition, revised and enlarged, published in 1963 by
Ure Smith Pty. Limited, 166 Phillip Street, Sydney
in association with
The Australian National Travel Association
18 Collins Street, Melbourne
Copyright the Australian National Travel Association, 1963
Printed in Australia by Waite & Bull Pty. Limited, Sydney
Registered in Australia for transmission
by post as a book

Contents

Illustrations

COLOUR PLATES

BLACK AND WHITE ILLUSTRATIONS

Introduction

In the pages which follow an attempt is made to supply a short guide which will tell something of the fascinating story of our best-known Australian coral reefs. It is very easy to show that there is far, far more of interest in our coral islands than is usually known, despite the glowing advertisements of the tourist departments. And what fascinates most does not appear in guide books nor in academic works and school books. The writer has always felt that it is a thousand pities that events which can be made exciting without untruth, or even exaggeration, remain unknown even to those who have visited or can visit the parts of Australia concerned. This is an attempt to set out a little of the story. It will, of course, be incomplete, for the material is enough for a thousand-page adventure. This is not surprising, for the relations between coral isles, their original inhabitants, and white men have always been varied – sometimes pleasant, sometimes disastrous. It is acting blindly, however, to be too dogmatic, even in these days when 'blue lagoons' can make stories into bestsellers. Human beings have the most varied tastes, and I have camped near tourists who were speaking in rapture of the beauty of the corals they had just seen on a tropic islet (even without understanding a lot about them) whilst their friends on the same afternoon and at the same place had actually preferred playing billiards! I raise no objections, however. Fishing and bathing are amongst the most delightful pastimes of the coral seas, and I suppose there may even be indoor games at the more highly developed resorts to ease a rainy day. It is the sum of the attractions of our coral regions which is of value, and in any case the naturalist will find that, owing to the tides, he can spend only a certain percentage of his time observing the characteristic sea creatures of coral reefs.

This book is accordingly written for the ordinary person, in the hope that it will answer many questions, and make the scenery more interesting and fascinating.

W.J.D.

Publisher's Note

The contents of this book originally appeared in 1950 as a series of six articles in the magazine *Walkabout*, written at the request of the Australian National Travel Association. They were written in the last few months of Professor Dakin's life, when he was seriously ill, but it was perhaps fitting that his life-long efforts to convey knowledge to others should have ended in that way. He died without seeing the letter of appreciation and thanks from *Walkabout's* editor. A little later the Australian National Travel Association decided to publish the whole series as a book. It first appeared in 1950, and was so popular that it was reprinted in 1953 and 1955. The present edition has been revised and enlarged.

1

Coral Islands and Coral Reefs

THE words coral and coral islands have generally called up visions of romance, and one remembers that they not only formed the background of many stories of boyhood, but have made best-sellers of more recent times. To scientists of the last hundred years they have, however, been magnets of great attractive power, and this attraction has not by any means ceased. They have provided the most fascinating problems for the marine biologist.

But opinions regarding the pleasant side of coral reefs have varied considerably. A well-known scientist, Professor Stanley Gardiner (formerly Professor of Zoology at Cambridge University, England), gave the following opinion, and Gardiner spent many months on coral islands: 'There is something in the psychology of mankind to which coral reefs never fail to appeal. The beauty of their immense wreaths of green, floating upon a sea, brilliant ultramarine in the hot sun, the whole dappled with the cloud shadows, is grateful to the voyager after weeks either of dull routine or of weary struggle in the trade winds. A visit ashore provides an interlude with fresh fish and coconuts, vegetables and fruit, and agreeable intercourse with handsome and friendly people such as are found in the South Seas.'

Gardiner had in mind the ring-shaped atolls of the tropics and those that were clothed with coconut palms and other vegetation. He added too that the interest and charm have been long recognized, for he quotes an early saying of the Chinese to the effect that coral reefs are 'waxing and waning like the life of man', and refers to the ancient Greeks and others collecting valuable products from the Red Sea coral reefs over two thousand years ago.

Another scientific writer of note, Professor F. Wood Jones, who lived on the Cocos Keeling Atoll for some time, referred to the halo of mystery with which the early navigators endowed the coral rings, and added, 'And when he came to know that the whole strange structure was the work of living creatures, he, following the lines of thought of his day, read into the whole the extraordinary human vanity of the lower creatures striving with ordered activity to create new fields for man's enterprises.' He also commented on the error which, even today, is often made: 'It is, I believe, a common enough idea that the coral creatures build coral, much as bees build honeycombs, but the comb is to them their dwelling place and their mausoleum, and the comb is raised up and up from the depths of the sea as the busy creatures build below.' Today even the school child, I hope, knows that there is no such act as building at all, and that to speak of a coral *insect* is completely absurd.

Professor C. M. Yonge, the British zoologist who spent a year on an island of the Great Barrier Reef area, also referred to the atolls of the Pacific in sparkling terms. 'These fairy rings of brilliant green foliage, enclosing placid lagoons, and arising as if by magic from bottomless oceans remote from land, were the cause of the wonder and admiration of early navigators, who, many weeks or months at sea, hailed with joy their exotic beauty and the calm waters of their sheltered lagoons.'

I am afraid there have been other views, and one of the first guides to the Barrier Reef states that ancient mariners never thought of coral as a thing of beauty or romance. To them 'it was a horror, a demon against which neither skill, nor care, nor knowledge, availed'.

I have heard many sarcastic references to the use of the word 'romantic', and usually they came from dull people who had most certainly never been thrilled by the sight of a coral island or by stories about them. But if romance is defined as the combination of beauty and strangeness, then one cannot deny that coral islands are amongst the most romantic spots on the earth's surface.

One of the first scientific writers on our subject, about a hundred years ago, also had hard words to say of coral isles, but he was also a good prophet, for he could not help concluding (even way back in those bygone days) with the remark, 'Still, if well supplied with foreign stores, including a good stock of ice, they might become, were they more accessible, a pleasant temporary resort for tired workers from civilized lands, who wish quiet, perpetual summer air, salt-water bathing, and boating or yachting; and especially for those who could draw inspiration from the mingled beauties of grove, lake, ocean, and coral meads and grottoes.'

This seems to have happened today. I must confess from my own experience that my sojourns on coral islands, whether on the atoll rings of the equatorial regions or those islets near our Australian coast, have given me some of the most delightful experiences of my life. But I can also appreciate the feelings of the wrecked sea-captain, or the survivors on a barren islet without population and with little water. I shall never forget a week of bad weather when I was anchored in a lagoon surrounded by islets of no charm and no population whatever. Our lives—or at least that of the ship—depended on two anchor chains and good holding on the coral bottom.

One feels that the great part played by coral islets in the literature of the last three centuries has been due largely to the romance and glamour of the opening up of the Pacific Ocean to certain trades. Those who have visited the great whaling museum of New Bedford cannot fail to realize how much the communication with the inhabitants of the coral islets of the Pacific meant to the young whalers. And the American whalers came to know practically every island of this ocean, not by any means to the good of the islanders.

But coral islands have had an advantage in respect of the exceedingly able and famous authors who have described them—and adventured on them too. One has only to think of such men as Robert Louis Stevenson, Pierre Loti and Herman Melville, or the works of Captain Cook, Captain Bligh, Dampier and other great seamen.

Only the north coast and the northern parts of the east and west coasts of Australia come into the region where coral flourishes, and we have no real coral ring-like 'green wreaths' in the surrounding ocean. But Australia is a continent of the most varied scenery both coastal and inland, and one of its world-famous features is the region of the Great Barrier Reef, which is the greatest coral growth of its kind.

This area provides all the beauty and also all the scientific puzzles for which man can wish, although to explain some of them we shall have to sidetrack a little to more distant scenes, including the coral atolls of the South Seas.

Since it is our intention here to produce a brief guide to Australian coral regions and their scenery, something which will interest visitors to those places, it is obvious that a serious attempt must be made to explain the nature of a coral growth. Without this the most beautiful vistas of coral would remain merely pictures of delicately coloured branching or non-branching sea-growths, round which a few gay fishes and crabs might be seen darting about. It is hoped, however, that the great scientific puzzle of the *formation* of coral reefs and islets may also add to the interest—even of the reader who never makes the happy journey to delectable islands.

There are different kinds of coral reefs, and the writer feels that it is much easier to explain the nature of their difference

Looking westward along the shore
at Heron Island.
Photo. Isobel Bennett.
Staghorn corals (*Acropora* spp.). *Photo. E. de Villa.*

than to proceed first to describe the coral animal itself.

You may be surprised at this, but it is quite easy to show by taking extracts from recent travel books (and writings by intelligent authors) that either our education or our use of the English language is responsible for some awful 'howlers' which have unlooked-for consequences. Much confusion hangs round the absurd use of the word 'insect'. You probably all know the old 'chestnut' about the railway porter who couldn't find the rates chargeable on a tortoise which a devoted father wished to send as a present. After looking up all his tables, the porter scratched his head, and confessed his complete failure with the words, 'Cats is dorgs, and dorgs is dorgs, but a tortoise is a hinseck!' This is nothing to the mistake of calling a coral animal an insect. And once you've done it, it's not a bit surprising getting into a worse mess.

How then can one tell an old mariner, or, if you like, a tired business man on a holiday, neither of whom has ever seen the coral animals, what a coral animal or a reef really is like—and without using scientific descriptions?

Well, firstly, a coral reef is a mass of limestone, and it may be several thousand feet thick—which makes it fairly obvious that most of it cannot be alive, or part of living creatures. It is, in fact, the remains of the skeletons and shells of animals, and plants too, which have lived during the thousands of years that the reef has been increasing in thickness. *On any coral reef, the living corals form only a thin skin, as it were, on the surface.*

Next, there is this matter of 'building' to settle. Coral animals do no more in secreting (or making, if you like) the hard limy part which is popularly known as coral than a snail does in producing its shell, or a human being in producing a skeleton. We don't know that we are producing ribs and leg bones as we grow up (until we are able to talk and someone tells us), and we cannot alter them by using our will. The coral animal is not even equipped with the senses of a snail,

17

for it comes at the lowest end of the animal kingdom—near the most primitive creatures of all. The coral skeleton is just a protective secretion of the animal's inner 'skin' and that is all there is to it.

For those who want to know more about the coral animal—and surely it is interesting to those who visit coral reefs to have some idea of the creature whose life helped to produce coral islands—we shall describe it in another chapter. But to make things a little clearer at this stage, let it be known that the coral creature is one of those animals which live an attached life, and it cannot possibly move after its young swimming embryonic stage has passed. Then, however, it begins not only to grow a little, but to increase its numbers by branching and budding like a plant. This is, of course, very strange indeed to most people who think of animals as creatures which run, walk, fly, swim or crawl. But there are many kinds of animals which live attached to rocks and ships, and no one would call a barnacle or an oyster anything but an animal, even though it never moves from its place of attachment.

One thing more you might like to know at this stage—the actual size of most reef-making corals is less than a quarter of an inch in diameter. No wonder the creature takes a little seeing. It was once calculated that there must have been 25,470 individuals on the surface of a piece of branched coral only two-thirds of a pound in weight.

So your coral reef, whether it be a submarine mountain, or only a low hill, is chiefly composed of the hard parts of animals and seaweeds which have lived their day. But they have left us their descendants, and some of the animals are forming a thin 'skin'—of countless millions—on the surface, and these are still adding to the thickness of the reef. (This is supposing that the conditions for life are still favourable in the sea at any particular point.)

Coral animals are not confined to the tropics. They can be

18

found growing in the temperate seas. It is in fact quite easy to find coral on the shore at Sydney, or from a few fathoms down in the harbour, and very extensive growths occur in some Norwegian fiords. But—and this is important fact number one—the extensive growth of coral to form reefs is a phenomenon of tropical seas. True reef-building corals are found only in the clear warm oceans of the tropics where the water is never colder than 20°C. (say 70°F.). But Australia possesses two highly exceptional coral regions—exceptional in that they are unusually far from the equator. On Lord Howe Island, between Australia and New Zealand, there is a coral reef along the western shore which makes a protected landing lagoon for flying-boats. The Abrolhos Islands, off the coast of Western Australia, are a very remarkable group of coral islands forty miles to sea opposite Geraldton; historically, too, this group is both interesting and exciting though the facts appear strangely unknown to many Australians. Both these coral regions may be regarded as unusual extensions of the northern coral reef areas. A poorly developed fringing reef was found not so long ago at Peel Island in Moreton Bay, a few miles from Brisbane, and quite a number of corals occur in other parts of that bay.

These occurrences can be explained only by assuming that there are warm ocean currents which keep the temperature within the proper limits at these latitudes. There is, of course, evidence for this. Probably, too, such currents carry the young of other sea creatures besides corals, because there are many interesting reef animals at Lord Howe Island which are found in the Great Barrier Reef area.

Important fact number two is that luxuriant growths of reef-building corals are only found in shallow waters— usually in depths not greater than 200 feet, with the best growths round 50 feet. This is a most startling fact, because it makes it difficult to explain how a coral islet can have grown in the distant ocean where the depths around the reefs are 5,000 or even 15,000 feet! It also provides us with a puzzle to explain our own Great Barrier Reefs, because the depths immediately outside at least those of the northern part are much greater than the depth at which reef coral grows. We shall have lots to say about this, perhaps the greatest scientific puzzle in the study of the oceans, in the last chapter.

Speaking generally, there are three kinds of coral reefs—fringing reefs, barrier reefs and atolls.

FRINGING REEFS

Since we have already stated that reef-building coral only grows in shallow water in warm seas, it would be natural to expect a growth of coral close to the seashore. This is correct and such reefs are called *fringing reefs*.

Coral grows up from the shallow bottom to the surface, but since it cannot in most cases withstand more than a little exposure to air, growth stops when it reaches the level of exposure at low tide. This has rather a curious effect on a tropical shore. If we look at the well-known surf beaches of Australia or indeed most of the continent's southern rocky shores, it will be seen that they slope gradually downwards. As the tide goes out the sea uncovers more of the slope—gradually. But where there are fringing reefs in the tropics the coral surface will be more or less level, and so as the tide falls one often sees quite suddenly a quick change in the amount of shore exposed. The water seems to run out very rapidly, and far, and the sandy shore ends in a kind of flat shelf, or *reef-flat*, as it is called. There will probably be many pools, and even a shallow lake or channel near the land where the shore ends and the reef-flat begins. But the channel will be suitable only for very small boats at low tide, and quite different from the lagoon behind a Barrier Reef to which we refer later.

There are plenty of fringing reefs round northern Australia, and indeed there are many round the islands inside what is usually called the Great Barrier Reef. There is nothing puzzling about these. Granted that the sea bottom is not too deep, and that water conditions are right, with the young of coral animals drifting in the sea, such coral reefs may start anywhere. They are the kind which the tourist will mainly visit for his fossicking. He can reach many on foot—taking care to wear sandshoes (even if he has nothing else but a hat! Scratches from coral are often nasty to heal). Other reefs may be submerged just enough so that they are best seen when viewed from glass-bottomed boats.

CORAL ISLANDS AS DISTINCT FROM CORAL REEFS

At this point a question suggests itself which may very likely be put forward by a traveller. If a coral reef only grows up to low or intertidal levels, how do coral islands originate? The visitor must be very careful about this. Many islands in the Great Barrier Reef area and elsewhere are big and high and are of igneous rock like granite. But they have fringing coral reefs round their shores (beautiful reefs, too, in many cases) because the coral finds a suitable place there to grow. Obviously these are *not* coral islands at all—notwithstanding. that they may give all the pleasure, or more, of coral islands. Tahiti, for example (to take an oceanic island), is of this kind.

A true coral island is usually low—a mere heap of broken-up coral fragments, or coral sand, on top of a base of coral. One often assumes that such islands originate through the sea piling up broken lumps of coral on top of a reef. Some of this becomes pulverized by the sea or even ground into sand by the action of living animals.

Possibly in many cases little coral islets owe their twenty or thirty feet or more of height above sea-level to changes in the level of the ocean which we know to take place. Naturally, a heap of sand would not exist for long on such coral foundation, but the rain may cement the limy particles, in fact 'beach rock' is the main feature ensuring permanency of many coral cays; birds may add excreta, and soon, seeds and plant growths reach them and bind the whole closer together. Of course, the plants have got to reach these islets, *which have grown up in the sea,* from somewhere else. Some germinating seeds like those of mangroves will stand a long bath of sea water. And birds may carry seeds on their claws or in their intestines. Ocean-drifting logs may bring a big share. Migrating human beings will be responsible for other additions. It is correct to say, however, that a true coral island which has originated from the sea will never have rich vegetation comparable to that often found clothing high continental islands such as Whitsunday Island or Hinchinbrook Island in the Barrier Reef channel. (See pages 45 and 46 for further reference to plants of Great Barrier Reef islands.) Strangest of all is the fact that there is still much argument about the coconut palms which we were told in our school days originated on distant coral islands from floating coconuts. Modern botanists admit, I think, at last that coconuts do *sometimes* commence in this way on coral islands, but still affirm that it is exceptional and that most have been deliberately planted by man.

BARRIER REEFS AND ATOLLS

Finally there is a type of coral growth which raises all sorts of peculiar problems. But first let me emphasize what we have done in setting down the title of this section. Firstly we have indicated that there is not one but a whole class of coral reefs in the sea referred to by scientists as 'barrier' reefs, and the Great Barrier Reefs are just examples of this class, although they may be regarded as the greatest. Secondly, we have implied that there is something similar between barrier reefs and atolls, yet an atoll is a more or less ring-like reef which is one of the most striking features of the tropical Pacific and East Indian oceans, and surely cannot be mistaken.

The explanation of this procedure is very important. It is simply that there *is* a feature which links barrier reefs and atolls together—they both are coral growths rising from deep water, and so quite different from fringing reefs. In fact, they offer us a startling problem in finding out how they began.

Having stated this, let us define a barrief reef. The name is given to a coral reef which rises some distance from land and leaves a channel or lagoon between it and the shore. The sea on the outside is deep and often slopes to great depths. With this as our definition it is certainly necessary to comment here on the manner in which the Great Barrier Reef differs from it, because there is a discrepancy. Most maps actually show the outer margin of the Great Barrier 'Reef' as one continuous reef. Large-scale charts give a better impression and it will be seen that in truth there is no single reef here at all. Instead we have a long string of separate reefs, which are not always in a line. The nearest approach to a regular wall of coral is made by the northern six hundred miles or so, where separate reefs lie in a line, with, for the most part, only narrow openings between them. It is usual for the lagoon inside a barrier reef to be twenty to forty fathoms in depth and from half a mile to ten or more miles wide. That of our Great Barrier Reefs averages about twenty-five fathoms, but the width, which varies, is far more, and at the widest part is over a hundred miles.

As a barrier reef is some considerable distance from the land and our Great Barrier Reefs certainly average thirty-five miles distance, there is no reason whatever why there should not be fringing reefs inside them—quite close to the land. In fact, inside the outer Great Barrier Reefs there are all sorts of coral growths, and there are hundreds of islands all with their own fringing reefs. This additional complexity has led to the area being sometimes called the Great Barrier *Reeferies*.

Barrier reefs usually run more or less parallel to coasts and in a line, like the exceedingly good example which runs parallel to the shore of New Caledonia not so far from Australia.

Since a barrier reef is a continuous reef or a line of reefs of coral which runs more or less parallel to a coastline but some distance away from it, there is no reason why there should not be such a growth round an island. There is, for example, a barrier reef round the island of Tahiti. This is the reason why we have coupled atolls with barrier reefs in this description. Take away the island (by the destructive action of the weather, or by its sinking under the sea) and you have an atoll.

We shall refer to all this again in a moment.

Most writers have let themselves go in describing the beauties of coral lagoons—the enclosed sea behind barrier reefs or inside atolls. From my own experience I can only add myself to their number. On days when the ocean is battering on the outside of the reefs, the lagoon surface may be calm and the water blue and of a clearness which is indescribable. On several occasions in England I have been asked how one could possibly find anything so beautiful in a stretch of water and some low land covered with palm trees, that the scene could be compared with either the miniatures of rural England or the magnificent pictures of the Alps and the Rockies. I described a day when I took a dinghy out on the calm water of a coral lagoon, and looking down at the bottom, which was sixty feet at least below me, felt quite frightened because there seemed to be no water at all supporting the dinghy. We seemed in fact to be in mid-air, and everything below and about us was just perfect in colour. I was more than surprised, whilst writing this account, to discover the following lines in a volume giving the life of the

Pisonia jungle, Heron Island. Note mutton-bird burrows in the foreground.

A coral pool with stagshorn and other corals.—*Photo Australian Museum.*

Nauru is an uplifted coral island with coconut palms clustered at its edge.

Coral exposed at low water. Species of *Acropora*—the branching staghorn cora's—
predominate in this photograph.

Exposed reef on the eastern shores of Hayman Island. —*Photo. Isobel Bennett.*

Collecting on a coral reef at low tide. The party has been brought to the reef edge by launch. *Photo. Frank McNeill.*

captain of a windjammer. He had landed on an atoll in the Pacific and described the scene as follows: 'We saw through the trees a beautiful lagoon and we made for it. I shall never forget the startling beauty of that lonely lagoon. It was fringed by pure white coral sand. Near the edge the water was as clear as crystal, and by that I mean that it *gave one the impression of not being there at all*. As it grew deeper it shaded gradually until eventually it was a deep but brilliant blue. No painter ever put such wonderful colouring on canvas.'

The statement which I have put in italics repeats my own impression—I wonder how many others have felt the same. Nearly a hundred years ago Wallace (later of Evolution fame with Darwin) wrote that 'The clearness of the water afforded me one of the most astonishing and beautiful sights I have ever beheld . . . For once, the reality exceeded the most glowing accounts I had ever read of the wonders of a coral sea.'

ATOLLS

To return to the atoll, the most striking of all coral formations in the Pacific and Indian oceans. These, as already stated, are ring-like reefs of coral which rise rather steeply from deep parts of the ocean. On the rim of the ring there are usually a series of little islets with passages between them giving entrance to the lagoon. The largest atoll of the world is one of the Maldive Island Group in the Indian Ocean, which covers an area of forty-two by thirty-two miles, and there are actually on its rim 102 little islets which are populated. Thus the number of channels into the lagoon of an atoll varies, and only a few may be navigable.

The famous so-called Cocos Keeling Island consists really of two separate atolls, Keeling Atoll and Cocos Atoll. The Keeling Atoll has almost the whole of its rim as land, and its lagoon is only a few feet deep with one opening to the ocean. The Cocos Atoll has twenty-four little islets and a corresponding number of passages into its lagoon.

But Australia has no real atolls of its own of any size for the reader to visit, so why mention them, you ask? The answer lies in the most important fact that it was in the attempt to explain the origin of atolls that information came enabling us to explain to some extent the possible origin of our own Great Barrier Reefs. In fact, as we shall see later, the theory of Darwin claims that an atoll was once a barrier reef round an island. Accordingly, the lagoon would occupy the place where the island once existed.

Summing up then we can say that Australia's coast touches the greatest coral sea area of the world. Indeed it is called the Coral Sea. On the coast itself we have fringing reefs of coral here and there all along the north coast, with many fine examples inside the outer line of reefs which form the Great Barrier Reefs proper. There are some coral reefs on the north-west coast, and there is a remarkable development of them farther south around the Abrolhos Islands of Western Australia. There is also a conspicuous fringing reef along the western shore of Lord Howe Island.

It is worth while emphasizing the fact that coral reefs are not equally developed along every shore in the tropics. Long ago it was noticed that the great continental land masses had extensive coral reefs only on their east coasts. Africa for example has them from the Red Sea southward and America has its famous West Indies and Florida areas.

The Indian Ocean and the western half of the Pacific are the seas where coral reefs flourish best. Probably the best explanation of these facts is still the theory that ocean currents and especially upwelling of cold water from the bottom along the west coasts of Africa and America make conditions unfavourable along the adjacent shores.

From the above it should be realized that reef-forming corals have played and will continue to play an enormously important part in the world's tropical seas. They are actually land builders since whole new islands may be formed or the shorelines of continents altered.

It has been estimated that some coral reefs have been in continuous existence for over fifty million years. One has only to see a storm on a tropical island to appreciate something of the enormous battering to which the seaward edge of a coral reef is constantly subjected. It has been estimated that *normal* waves dissipate 500,000 horse-power against the weather side of an ocean atoll, and the force of storm waves is infinitely greater.

Yet lowly animals and plants have been responsible for these structures, which continue to grow and withstand such forces. No wonder then that these most extensive of marine communities continue to excite and puzzle the scientist and engineer of today.

2

The Great Barrier Reef or Reeferies

As ALREADY mentioned the name 'reeferies' was given to our subject long ago because there is no long continuous barrier reef facing the ocean like a wall, as it is marked on many maps, and it is surely unsuitable to refer in the singular to this, the greatest coral development in the world with its hundreds of islands and its maze of reefs.

For the tourist, and indeed the scientist, too, it is more appropriate to consider as a whole the area covering about 80,000 square miles which presents such magnificent coral growths and which lies between the Queensland coast and an outer line of reefs running for roughly twelve hundred miles from Papua to just south of the tropic of Capricorn.

THE OUTER BARRIER

We have already defined a barrier reef as a coral reef growing some distance from land, so that it forms a 'break-water' or 'barrier off the shore' with a natural channel or lake inside it, called a lagoon, deep enough for ships. And its outer side rises from deep water where no reef-building corals live. We might, on this definition, think of the name Great Barrier Reef as applying to the long outer boundary of our area. It is most like one reef in its northern part, where it is a remarkable line of reefs stretching end to end for six hundred miles down to the latitude of Cairns. And these reefs rise steeply from ocean depths of 6,000 feet or more on the outside. The rest of the outer boundary, southward to the Swain Reefs, which are usually regarded as marking the southern extremity of the Great Barrier 'Reef', consists of a number of irregularly scattered reefs.

We can simplify our description if we consistently speak of this twelve hundred miles of reefs, which are more or less in a line facing the great and almost ever-present rollers of the Pacific, as the *reefs of the outer barrier*, and use the expression Great Barrier Reefs to cover them. But we should never forget the difference between the northern six hundred miles and the southern continuation. There is a very convenient large break in this outer barrier making an opening for big ships and dividing the northern from the southern half. This is the Trinity Opening, opposite Cairns. There are other openings suitable for navigation, besides the little breaks.

The reefs of the outer barrier are almost all visible at low water (probably with water streaming across them on most days), and a visit to one of them is likely to be highly dramatic. A good navigator and a wise seaman are very necessary, and our stay will probably last only a fraction of an hour and be possible only when the tide, the sea and the weather generally are very favourable.

Once again we emphasize the fact that the line of reefs of the outer barrier is closely backed up as it were by an absolute maze of scattered reefs and channels on the inner side.

Most of these reefs do not rear themselves up above tide levels as islands, even as 'low' islands. It is customary, at least in official pilotage reports and scientific descriptions to use the term 'cay' for islands in our area which result from the accumulation of coral sand or coral fragments on a reef. (Thus Heron Island consists of a relatively small sand cay situated at the north-west end of a reef whose outline is visible, especially from the air, at low water.) The word cay

37

is derived from the Spanish *cajo*, and is the same as the term 'key' on the coast of Florida. In many books on the Great Barrier Reef it is simply stated that a low coral island is termed a 'cay' when it is 'a solid island without a lagoon', in contrast to ring-shaped atolls. We must leave it at this or we shall make confusion worse confounded. It is quite appropriate for that part of our coral islands which is above water at high tide and conveniently distinguishes such islands from their reef-flats which are only exposed at low water.

A REEF OF THE OUTER BARRIER

To land on one of these reefs and make the visit a success, one needs low spring tides and a flat ocean surface. You will be lucky if you have both.

Roughly speaking, the reef above water is like a long platform in the sea—probably several miles long if we take an example from the part north of Cairns. Looked at from the air, one would see that the surface was marked by a series of zones, all parallel to the outer edge. The order of these as seen on one of the reefs is indicated in the diagram of a section (page 65). Let us, however, describe the conditions as the writer has seen them; there are probably considerable differences according to the locality.

Assuming you have the lucky day, it is profitable to leave your launch in good hands, and to make across the reef to the outer edge at once. This is not the highest part of the reef. There is usually a slight slope downward to the extreme edge and this strip, which may be anything up to a hundred and fifty feet or so wide, is often 'scalloped', that is to say, cut in every here and there by little valleys. The safest place (keeping a very watchful eye open for an unusual swell) to see things on the outer slope is probably at the edge of one of these valleys. Here one may look down, as it were, into the abyss, as the startingly clear and blue water surges up and down, and see some of the branched corals growing. (Professor W. Stephenson of the Zoology Department, Queensland University, who viewed this underwater scene with goggles, describes it as 'a marvellous sight—the most impressive of all "views" I have *ever* seen').

All the time, little waterfalls of draining sea water run off from the reef. But the most striking feature is the nature of the surface of the scalloped edge. In contrast to the blue water it varies from pink to purple, and with extensive smooth patches which look as if someone had covered the surface with a layer of pinkish cement. This marginal strip is in reality covered thickly with an encrustation of pinkish limy plants, mainly of species called *Porolithon* and *Lithophyllum*. These encrusting algae actually play a very important role in stabilizing coral reefs, but it is very difficult to explain their nature to the non-scientific person, who expects a plant to have branches and leaflets and not be a plain layer of hard limy stuff covering a flat surface.

Inside the 'edge zone' (which is apparently not always the same as the example I am describing), the reef rises slightly to its highest part. This zone, which is known as the crest runs almost like a rough carriage drive the length of the reef and parallel to the edge. It is comparatively smooth, which is not surprising, seeing that on most days a surf will be breaking on the outer edge and waves will constantly flow over the whole reef to the lagoon inside. The reef-crest may be one hundred to two hundred feet wide, and because of its smoothness is not a place where one lingers to look for growing corals. There are a few here and there, but on the whole they are small, stunted growths. There may, however, be a few pools which are worth a glance.

In most places it is difficult to detect the inside boundary of the reef crest, because it slopes imperceptibly, and only by inches, to a level area which makes up most of the reef surface above water at low tide. And this reef-flat changes slowly in character as one wades across it towards the inner lagoon. At some point one begins to find that it is covered with boulders of coral. These have been flung over from the outer edge of the reef and carried by the waves until far enough from the edge for the force of the waves to have been lost (except on occasions when higher seas are running). So there is what may be called a *boulder zone*. It has been recognized on most ocean coral reefs, near and far from Australia.

The boulder zone is quite interesting and becomes more so as one passes inwards, for the surface of the reef has depressions everywhere, and the boulders lying in them hide all sorts of quaint creatures—starfish, crabs, bêche-de-mer, trochus and other mollusc shells, which shelter from the terrific surf that batters the region at the extreme outer edge. Gradually as one passes still further inward (towards the launch one has left behind) the water deepens, and here and there are bigger pools with sandy bottom. Very rich growths of coral and soft coral will be seen here. Finally one has to wade deeply and the lagoon of our anchorage is reached. Our visit to the real barrier is over.

To get the appropriate thrill down one's spinal column when seeing the above, one ought to have been previously near enough to the outer barrier on a day when the sea is *not* calm. This gives a far greater respect for the lowly creature whose growth can withstand such battering of the ocean, and causes one to keep a weather eye open whilst inspecting what is usually hidden by the restless sea.

THE REEFS AND ISLANDS OF THE GREAT BARRIER REEF CHANNEL

There are hundreds of islets of the Barrier Reef Channel, some of which are true coral islands in the sense that they have originated as coral growths from the sea bottom, whilst

Burrowing clams (*Tridacna fossar*) are common among dead and living corals on the reef flat.
Photo. Paul Roach.

others—the continental islands—are of granite and other igneous rocks like those of the nearby mainland, and so are entirely different. We remind the reader once again of the difference between islands and reefs. There are many coral reefs which are always submerged as well as others which just reach tide level. They are not only dangerous for shipping, but may trouble amateur fishermen. South of Cairns, in particular, the greatest concentration of such submerged coral reefs, as well as reefs bearing cays, lies to the eastward (outer side) of the Barrier Reef Channel. This arrangement is outstanding. The pilotage of the outer area of reefs and islets is best left to local fishermen and to the regular collectors of trochus shell and bêche-de-mer, who know the dangers and pass through these waters by day with a good look-out posted as high as possible. The best way of preventing shipwreck is by the 'look and see' method of navigation, and this is not possible when the sun is low and reflected from the surface water.

Let us now turn to the islands proper which are notable features of this area and of which, as indicated, there are two very distinct classes. It is a striking fact that these barrier reef islands should be of two entirely different types which are roughly arranged along two lines in their proximity and general relationship to the mainland.

The true coral islands, which, as noted above, have arisen by the growth of living creatures from the bottom of the sea, are often called *low islands*. In most cases, their substance above sea-level can be accounted for by the heaping up of coral debris, sand and other sea materials, and is only a matter of a few feet. Indeed Heron Island, one of the best-known today—by reason of its holiday facilities—is only about fifteen feet in height and it is the highest of the Capricorn Group. Gradually the action of the atmosphere changes the nature of the surface. Limy sand may be consolidated into beach rock, and then nature gets to work again and through one means or another plants will reach the new land which has originated from below the sea.

The origin of the continental islands is a different matter altogether. Such islands as Lindeman Island, Whitsunday Island, Hinchinbrook Island and Magnetic Island are relics of high land which was once part of the Queensland mainland, from which it has been separated by changes in sea level.

This does not prevent the continental islands from being visited by tourists or even scientists wishing to study coral, because in the first place there are usually fine fringing coral reefs growing round their shores, and in the second place some have excellent tourist facilities and are very beautiful and attractive. They often provide amenities for more permanent residence (although some may argue about this).

Islands of this type often rise hundreds or even thousands of feet above sea level. The famous Hinchinbrook Island has peaks over 3,000 feet high and reaches up to a point over 3,500 feet. Such islands are most picturesque and are often clothed with dense jungle. It must not be forgotten that there are also some small and low islands which go with this type—their basis being granite and not coral. The distinction is simple and the existence of small rocky islets off a sea-coast is not confined to the area we are now speaking about.

According to specialists, the true coral islands of the Great Barrier Reef area can be classified as of several different sub-types. For example, in the Capricorn Group itself some consist mainly of coarse shingle and others of sand. The Capricorn and Bunker islands are also sometimes regarded as different from the others because they are really south of the Great Barrier Reefs and very exposed to the ocean. Then some coral islands in the northern part can be recognized as different again, and are frequently called *low wooded islands* Curiously enough their ground plans show that each consists as it were of two raised parts, a sand cay to leeward and a mangrove swamp and shingle island (or ridges) to windward. Low Isles, about forty miles north of Cairns, are a textbook diagram of this particular type of structure.

Such details as these are for the student of physiography, and in any case, the specialists don't always agree. We just mention the fact here in case the reader happens to see some reference to different kinds of islands. We don't want him to have his attention drawn from the fact that there are two basic types of islands and that when we refer to these we mean, on the one hand, all low coral islands whose base is coral, and on the other, isolated fragments, high or low large or small, of the mainland, which are to be classed with the small islets anywhere off the coast of Australia and whose origin has nothing to do with coral growth.

It is stated that in the Great Barrier Reef Channel no less than six hundred islets are large enough to be worthy of recognition in the records of the Queensland Lands Department. This figure includes both the true coral islands and those of the continental type, but it is impossible at this state of our own knowledge to give exact figures of either the number or nature of the barrier reef islets.

Where it occurs, the vegetation on these low coral islands is of a limited nature and is related chiefly to those types of plants which are adapted to drifting over the sea, or carriage by birds. Mangroves, however, are more common on the northern cays, and in a few cases man has planted coconut palms. One naturally expects the number of species of both animals and plants living on continental islands to be far greater than on coral islands. High islands like Hinchinbrook, for example, are far more ancient than the coral cays and their dense vegetation is related to the tropical rain forests of the mainland of which they were once a part. Their wildernesses have remained unaltered by the changes in sea-level.

The scientist looks for most interesting creatures on such islands, because isolation seems to be one of nature's methods of changing species and modifying the original types. Unfortunately the hand of man has in some cases considerably altered the original scenic picture by clearing and farming or by the introduction of domestic animals, especially goats, as food for shipwrecked mariners.

HERON ISLAND AND OTHER CORAL ISLANDS OF THE BARRIER REEF

A few comments on some of the best-known true coral islets which would be seen in passing from south to north up the Barrier Reef Channel may be of interest. The southernmost low islands are, on the whole, rather similar in structure, although they vary in size and the nature of their vegetation. The surface may be of sand, shingle, or so-called beach or coral rock, or a combination of all three. As the tide goes out, however, there comes a point when the basic reef is exposed (possibly all round) and the 'island' suddenly becomes much larger. This is a striking feature. The rather sudden appearance of a fringing reef at low tide and its extent are always surprising, but much more so round low islands, where its area may be much greater than that of the cay—the part above water at high tide. Some of these islands have been built up in such a way that the surrounding fringing coral reef actually encloses something like a shallow lagoon. They cannot be called true atolls because this name is now usually reserved for ring-shaped coral reefs rising from very deep ocean water (see Chapter 6), whereas these islets in the Barrier Reef Channel are only surrounded by depths of ten to twenty-five fathoms, the average for the channel inside the outer barrier.

It will be remembered that the Barrier Reef Channel is about a hundred and fifty miles wide at its southern end, where it is rather open since the outer barrier ends in scattered reefs—the Swain Reefs. South of this latitude are the southern coral cays of the Capricorn and Bunker groups.

Ships passing north can either steam altogether outside the Barrier Reef, or enter the channel near the Capricorn Group, then take a charted track (the longest stretch of pilotage in the world) which leads through the Whitsunday Passage.

Heron Island is one of the largest coral islands of these groups, but this does not mean that it is of great size, for the actual cay is only about three hundred yards across (practically north–south) and half a mile long (longest diameter approximately east-west). The cay itself, which is situated on the extreme north-western side of its basic coral platform, consists almost entirely of sand. On both the northern and southern shores the sand has been partly converted into the characteristic beach rock already mentioned. The amount of this rock visible in any one year seems to vary according to the cyclonic disturbance in the area. There has been considerable argument about the mode of formation of beach rock and some scientists think it is chiefly due to the action of rain and atmosphere, whilst others regard its origin as a more complicated story.

The most striking feature to the visitor is the remarkably thick covering of high trees in the middle of the island. This makes Heron Island and one or two others of the Capricorn Group curiously attractive. In this respect Heron may be considered as a fully developed coral islet. The centre of the island has reached the tree stage and is covered with a dense jungle of pisonias, remarkably massive-looking, heavily branched trees attaining heights of sixty feet. The contrast between the green shade of this jungle and the hot white sand in the blazing sun is almost indescribable. No photographer can abstain from using up film on the scenes amidst these large-leafed trees. The pisonia-tree is however, a 'snare and a delusion'. The thick branches with their very large leaves are sappy and snap like cabbage stalks under even a moderate weight. The pisonia jungle can be a fascinating place for another reason—its occupation by thousands of sea-birds during the nesting season. At such times, both sea and land join in presenting interests quite foreign to the visitor from colder climes.

On the outside of the pisonia area, there is a marginal belt of casuarina-trees (sheoaks), and the silver-leafed *Tournefortia*. The 'photogenic' pandanus palms with their 'prop' roots grow in positions suitable for the amateur photographer for whom they provide favourite foregrounds or backgrounds according to the nature of his picture. There are a few coconut palms on these southern low coral islands, all hand planted.

Mangroves are more striking features on the coral islets of the northern parts of the Great Barrier Reef and are not found on the Capricorns. Several shrubs are frequent on sand cays like Heron Island, the most common ones being *Scaevola koenigii* and *Wedelia biflora*. The creepers which roam over the sand are probably to be counted amongst the first kinds of plants to take a hold on a 'newly born' coral islet. Tourists to these coral islands, appreciating that they have arisen as it were from below the sea, frequently ask how trees like the pisonia reached them. The answer is that some part of the plant is specially suited for drifting over the sea, being blown by the wind, or carried by birds (that is of course if human beings have not had a hand in the business, by accident or by design). The convolvuli creeping over the sand have buoyant seeds not affected easily by sea water. The sheoaks probably came as seeds blown by the wind, for the little seeds have a thin wing which is specially adapted for dispersal in this way. The pisonia-trees are dispersed by birds which nest or alight on the branches, for they have fruits which are extremely sticky and which stick to the feathers or legs. In fact, they are a bit too efficient and small birds may die as the result of the sticky substance gumming up their feathers. Mangrove fruits are famous for their long resistance to sea water as they are floated about by sea currents.

During the year, chiefly the months from spring to summer, various islands of the reef channel are chosen by sea-birds for their nesting places. Heron Island is fortunately one of these and it is favoured in particular by the white-capped noddy terns and the mutton-birds (wedge-tailed shearwaters).

The noddy terns take possession of the pisonia-trees where they nest on the branches with nests of fallen leaves. Perhaps more startling to the visitor unacquainted with the seashores of Australia are the mutton-birds, which arrive during the last three months of the year and nest underground. Mutton-birds are oceanic birds known to ornithologists as shear-waters. On the island their nests are made below the pisonia-trees in the sand and at the end of rather shallow burrows reminescent of rabbit burrows.

The visitor to a coral island such as Heron should go roaming about at night as well as by day if he wishes to see everything possible. Thus-wise he will appreciate the interest-ing habits of the mutton-bird, which leaves its nesting place in the early morning and is absent during the day feeding out on the ocean. As darkness follows twilight the mutton-birds return—maybe in thousands—finding their burrows in some mysterious way, but sometimes getting a little confused on their route through the pisonia jungle. And then the tree-covered part of this island can produce the effects of a bad nightmare, with an accompaniment of noises which even a modern orchestra would find it difficult to imitate. By daybreak, the food-providing sea-birds have departed once again on the hunt and the island is relatively empty. But don't forget the herons which fish the coral pools on the reef-flat and nest in the pandanus-trees, and keep an eye open for that true coral islander—the frigate-bird—with its forked tail. Here, it is the lesser frigate-bird (*Fregata minor*). On Australia's mandated coral island of Nauru, the frigate-birds are domesticated by the natives, but it appears that they are merely kept as pets. They have been used, like pigeons, as carriers of messages between some Pacific islands. One bird expert describes them as possibly the most completely aerial of all water birds, 'and perhaps of all birds except swifts'.

There is another mutton-bird which nests in the sand on the islands of Bass Strait, but this is the short-tailed shearwater and not the same species as the mutton-bird (the Wedge-tailed Shearwater) of the Capricorn and Bunker groups, which happens also to breed in the sands of the Western Australian Abrolhos Islands. There may be hundreds of thousands of these mutton-birds, some say millions, on the small area of a few of these islands. Walking over the sand becomes a nightmare, as one may go through the surface to the knees or even thighs at almost every other step. The life habits of these birds (both the noddy terns and the mutton-birds) are amongst the most extraordinary of this delightful animal group.

No description of Heron Island or others of the Capricorn Group could be complete without reference to the great green turtles which congregate at night and lay their eggs on shore in the summer months. Turtles of several species frequent the northern coral seas, but the best known are the loggerhead, the hawksbill and most especially the green turtle. The first-named is not sought after. The hawksbill is valuable for the so-called tortoise shell of commerce. The green turtle has long been recognized for its edible qualities and because of this and its abundance on some coral shores has achieved a degree of fame which has been accentuated by the tales told about it. A special study of the green turtles visiting Heron Island was made by F. W. Moorhouse, M.Sc., who made and published a full report. The turtles visit the island after dark and parades take place practically every night from the end of October to February. By marking some of the turtles it has been discovered that one and the same

A female Lesser Frigate-Bird (*Fregata minor*) and below, a female Least Frigate-bird (*F. oriel*) with a six-weeks-old chick. *Photos. Dr. Gibson-Hill.*

Heron Island, with submerged coral surrounding it.
This aerial photograph looks west towards the mainland.

Pandanus palms, Heron Island.

Terns, Michaelmas Cay, Cairns.

Prop roots of pandanus palms, Heron Island; and (below) Green turtle.

female will visit the same island several times (up to seven times has been recorded) for egg-laying during the season.

A female finds its way heavily over the sand to a point above high-water mark, leaving a track made by the flippers as characteristic as that of an army tank. Having reached a height and place which seems suitable, she 'flips' the sand out with her fore-flippers and piles it behind, using the hind-flippers until a hollow of the right depth and size to fit her body has been made. And then occupying this hollow and using the hind-flippers only, she excavates a much smaller pit—the egg pit—in which the eggs will be laid. Moorhouse gives the number as approximately 120 for one laying, though a range from 66 to 195 was observed. When the eggs are laid and the egg pit filled, the 'nest' is filled in, the flippers working until the level of the sand is once more almost uniform and the presence of the excavation obliterated.

Imagine fifty-one animals seen arriving on one night! Moorhouse points out that whilst many thousands of eggs are laid, the number of turtles visiting the islands has been overestimated seriously because of the lack of recognition of the return in one season by the same animal on several occasions.

The eggs of the green turtle take about nine and a half to ten and a half weeks to hatch (leaving the nest takes place usually at nightfall), and then comes the remarkable journey to the sea, the little turtles recognizing in some way the direction of the water and heading for it unless attracted by a bright light. Unfortunately a great percentage fall victims, as do other young animals, to their special enemies. On land, these include birds by day and large crabs by night, but this is only the beginning, and in the sea, sharks and other fish complete the sad story. It is obviously not difficult for man, by over-catching the adults, to put the finishing touches and upset completely the balance of nature.

Some of the highly decorative pamphlets issued by the

tourist bureaux show young men and bright young things 'riding' turtles on the shores of the Capricorn Islands. The riders do not often stay long on the backs of the animals when in the water but this exciting form of entertainment is a fact, nevertheless.

Turning now to the sea, which after all is the more important interest for us, we draw attention again to the amazing difference between the appearance of Heron Island at high and low tide, especially on the dates of spring tides.

For some hours the island is just the more or less oval sand cay we have described. But suddenly, as the tide recedes, the coral basis of the island shows itself. This is spoken of as the reef-flat. At high tide it is all covered by the sea and boats drawing only a few feet of water sail over it and land passengers at the sandy beach. At low water there are acres of very rough coral surface on which to go 'fossicking'. Some of it is, however, rather rotten coral and one must be careful not to go through into a pool of unexpectedly deep water, with nasty scratches accompanying the catastrophe. Above all, don't get stranded on it.

The writer has been personally acquainted with members of parties suffering two different kinds of trouble dependent on the rapid flow of the oncoming tide over coral reef-flats. In the first case the party got too far from its dinghy, when the tide had receded, forgetting in the excitement of their collecting that one cannot travel quickly over coral. They also forgot the time. When they were alarmed by the returning tide the position was dangerous and their return to their dinghy most unpleasant.

In the other case a party took a launch to visit a little coral island (waterless), timing their arrival when they could sail over the reef-flat to the shore of the cay. Members of the party did not appear at the time set for the refloating of the launch. Unfortunately they had omitted to notice that the next tide was not as high (a marked feature of the east

Australian coast), and so the party had to wait over a long period (two tides) without food and water until the reef-flat was navigable.

The coral reef-flat extends all round Heron Island, but it is very unequally developed on the different sides. On the eastern side its distant seaward margin must be five or six miles away from high-water mark, or what one might call the 'land'. This position of a sandy cay nearer one end or side of its coral base is fortunate for the fossicker, for it is only half a mile or so's walk to the seaward edge of the reef-flat on the north-west side in front of the settlement. On the south-east it looks as if the reef extends away for ever and its edge can be reached safely only with a launch. A considerable part of the reef-flat at Heron is sandy with dead coral boulders scattered over it. But even here the careful searcher will find much of interest. And there are small colonies of various living corals which become larger and more numerous (both in size and species) as one gets closer to the outer edge of the reef.

If you have never walked over a coral reef-flat, take a little care. Boots or sandshoes are best, but at least you must have shoes which will not come to pieces, and preferably some sort of covering such as thick socks on the legs. The reef will reveal an amazing store of wonders. It consists of living coral, dead coral, and sandy pools which are like superlative aquaria with little fish and quaint creatures of many kinds and surprisingly brilliant colours. Don't forget to turn over any loose blocks of coral. Most of the active animals like crabs, shrimps and fish, dislike the garish exposure to sunlight when the tide goes out, and they hide where ever possible.

By reason of the position of the Capricorn Group at the open southern end of the Great Barrier Reef Channel, the east and south-east margins of the reef-flat of Heron Island are rather fully exposed to the open sea. In fact this makes the Capricorn reefs rather similar to a reef of the outer

59

barrier proper, which is a great advantage from the point of view both of the scientist and the tourist.

Everyone who has visited Heron Island and its nearby neighbours comments on the clearness of the water and its freedom from silt. Except where they have been damaged by cyclones the coral growths are particularly fine. This may be due to the proximity of the open sea, or to this freedom from land silt, which may still be regarded as injurious to reef corals.

The pools on the reef-flat vary in depth and join up here and there, and there is a fairly extensive depression near the island in front of the settlement on the northern side, which retains a foot or so of water when the tide is low. This has perhaps unfortunately come to be called the lagoon, by tourists. We say unfortunately, because there is a deeper and more extensive depression with permanent sea on the east side of the island where the flying-boats used to land. This latter is a much closer approximation to a *true* coral-island lagoon.

This is really important because it raises the question, 'Why not call Heron Island an atoll? Lady Musgrave Island not so far away also has a lagoon, but these islands like Pelsart Island of the Abrolhos Group (which looks still more like a true atoll—see the map), are not regarded as atolls, because they do not 'peak up' from oceanic depths but only rise from a moderately shallow sea bottom.

The visitor who has gone to a coral island to see something of its marine wonders will spend much time 'playing about' on the reef-flat. It takes years to exhaust the interest of such an area if one has an expert as guide, and we recommend the excitement which can result from trying to photograph the scenes instead of making illegal collections of specimens which even the expert cannot preserve without their beauty being lost. Even professional zoologists have forgotten how little we know of the habits of life of many coral-reef animals and the need for watching their little ways far exceeds that of bottling specimens.

Near the margin of the reef-flat one should notice the different zones which run parallel to the edge. There is on the weather side of most of the reefs of the Capricorn Group a reef-crest such as that already described on the outer barrier, though it may not be more than twenty feet or so across. Behind this cross is a boulder zone with curious rough pillar-like blocks of dead coral called 'niggerheads'. These have once been coral growths projecting up from the sea bottom, near the reef margin. They have been torn loose in some more than usually heavy storm and hurled on to the reef-flat, where they may stand for many years, gradually being eroded by sea and atmosphere, and often black through the growth of lichens. Shorewards lies the more sandy reef-flat.

The most common animals of the coral-reef pools are referred to later, and it may be noted that they are practically the same whatever island be visited in the region we are describing.

The Capricorn and Bunker coral islands have possibly played the greatest part of any in the furthering of scientific studies of Australian coral reefs (at least until the expedition from England, 1927–8, camped for a year on Low Isles to the north of Cairns). Masthead Island used to be one of the favoured spots for the simple camps of the earlier scientific visitors. Like Heron Island it is well clothed with vegetation, and possibly is even a better haunt for sea-birds.

Passing northward, we should see other low coral islands, but many of them are much less attractive on shore than those of the Capricorn Group already named. They may be merely heaps of coral sand or shingle with a few creeping plants holding the material together, or their vegetation may be low shrubs or grasses, or there may be no vegetation at all (Sudbury Cay). They may rise only one or two feet above sea-level and suffer badly from heavy seas in a storm. Most will have little or no interest for the tourist, although they may have interest for scientists who are able to visit them. Several bear lighthouses.

We can pass these by and travel hundreds of miles northward, ignoring also for the moment the numerous and exceedingly beautiful rocky continental islands, until we reach Cairns, before we meet other low coral islands which have become well known as tourist centres. North of Cairns one or two of the low islands have become known for special reasons. First there is Green Island, about eighteen miles north-east of Cairns, which is a National Reserve and, with its underwater observatory, a centre for visitors. Slightly farther north, but lonely now, its small size and lack of vegetation offering no attraction to tourists, is the small Michaelmas Cay, which is mentioned because it is one of the places where a boring was made to find the thickness of coral material (See Chapter 6.)

Apart from this fact, Michaelmas Cay (and Oyster Cay not so far away) is also noted as an amazing place for the nesting of sea-birds in their season. The entire sandy beach surface is just crowded with little concavities which is all the nest that sooty terns and caspian terns make. (See page 54.) As a matter of fact, the huge number of birds nesting on these cays in October, and the lack of room, would in itself make a sojourn here in tourist style quite impossible during what is the most favourable weather season of the year. Charles Barrett, who knew these two low islands well, stated that the eggs used to be collected by aborigines, but these cays are now sanctuaries.

North of these is Low Isles (the real name as well as the type), which became famous for the encampment of the British Museum's scientific expedition in 1927-8. Full details of their story are given by Professor Yonge in his book, *A Year on the Barrier Reef*. In 1954 the Queensland

Great Barrier Reef Committee organized and equipped another expedition to Low Isles. This included botanists, geographers, geologists and zoologists, and the objective was completely to re-survey the island in the light of the British Expedition's work of twenty-five years ago so that some idea might be gained of the growth or changes in a coral reef covering a period of a quarter of a century.

CONTINENTAL OR ROCKY ISLANDS OF THE BARRIER REEF AREA

The continental islands are arranged chiefly as little chains or festoons of islets approximately parallel to the Queensland coast and chiefly between the latitude of Gladstone in the south and Bowen in the north. Others continue the series until the long known but infrequently visited Lizard Island of Captain Cook is reached, north of Cairns.

It must be confessed that the outstanding photogenic seascapes of the Queensland coast are to be found amidst these rocky islets, and the geologist probably finds them more interesting than the true coral islets of which we have just spoken. The Whitsunday Passage and its bounding islets are very justly famous, and people all the world over have spoken to me of the glorious scenery of this group. The islands of the Whitsundays are arranged in two series. One chain lies to the east of the steamship passage, and includes Hayman, Hook, Whitsunday, Lindeman, Shaw and part of the long chain of the Cumberland Islands stretching away to the south. The other chain of islands, including North, West and South Molle islands, and Long Island lies to the west of this passage and thus nearer the land, and it is because of this biserial arrangement that the famous steamship passage comes into being. This is part of the main shipping track along the coast, and it faces southward almost like a funnel, so that it is not altogether surprising that

63

Captain Cook found himself safely cruising northward with islets to left and right of him.

Most of the islands rise to heights above 600 feet and are well wooded. Hook Peak is, however, 1,478 feet high and this large island and Whitsunday Island, which is bigger still and has at least three peaks over 1,000 feet high, are relatively inaccessible. Magnificent cliffs are developed, usually on the eastern margin, and some fringing coral reefs are present in the bays. Tourist centres have been set up on several of the islands of the Whitsunday Group and the visitor might almost think he was on the mainland if it were not for the sea or air trip needed in order to reach his destination.

In the Whitsunday Group excellent fringing reefs are exposed here and there for the fossicker at low tide, despite the fact that these are rocky continental islands. The reefs usually are to be found in the bays. Fortunately not all the shores develop coral reefs, otherwise conditions would not be so generally favourable for the different pastimes enjoyed. There are smooth stretches of coral sand where small seine nets may be hauled without the risk of tearing by unseen coral, and such beaches are really essential for pleasant bathing.

There are so many fascinating spots that it is only possible to leave their discovery to information obtained from local residents willing to act as guides.

The Molle Islands are a group of about six altogether and are composed of volcanic rocks. Perhaps the fringing reefs are not so well developed as on some of the eastern islands which are situated somewhat nearer the outer barrier, but there are fringing reefs in some of the bays which can easily be reached.

Northward from the Whitsunday Group there are very many other rocky islets with fringing coral reefs before Townsville is reached. It is not possible to mention any in

Denman Island from the hill, South Molle Island. Whitsunday Island is seen in the distance across the Passage.

Lagoon with coral pinnacles   Boulder Zone   Reef Crest   Outer edge   Ocean

Diagram of a section through an outer reef of the Great Barrier Reefs.

Tournefortia argentea, one of the characteristic trees of the Great Barrier Reef Islands. (Below) White-capped Noddy on nest in pisonia tree, Capricorn Islands. —*Photos, Isobel Bennett.*

detail. Middle Island in Edgecumbe Bay actually played a part in the battle between supporters of the chief rival coral reef theories. It was visited in 1896 by the famous American A. Agassiz—a great exponent of the Darwin hypotheses described in Chapter 6.

One might also mention that there are several reefs and islets easily reached from Bowen, which is just north of Edgecumbe Bay.

About a hundred and forty miles or so north of the Whitsunday Group is Townsville, and very close to this point is the rocky Magnetic Island. Like other rocky islands of the reef channel it is beautiful with its delightful bays, its swimming beaches, its coral growths and its vegetation, but perhaps it is just too much of a great holiday resort for Townsville. One scarcely feels that one is an adventurer in a coral-reef zone when bathing in one or other of its much frequented bays. But the writer must admit that on more than one occasion during World War II he blessed the easy access to Magnetic Island. One could almost forget about suffering under its shady palm-trees. And there was a garden with the most beautiful bougainvillea—colours never forgettable.

North of Magnetic Island one should mention the group of the Palm Islands which form an aboriginal reserve. There are between a thousand and fifteen hundred natives here, with churches and two schools, altogether an excellent organization and admirably situated.

No account of the Great Barrier Reef area would be complete without a reference to Hinchinbrook Island and the Hinchinbrook Channel. And this would not be on account of coral, for Hinchinbrook could scarcely be called a good centre for coral island studies. Hinchinbrook is very close to the mainland of Queensland; in fact it is a long island with its long axis running north and south, and separated only by the narrow channel of the same name.

But Hinchinbrook Island is the centre of some of the finest seascapes of the whole world. Despite its moderate size it has high, precipitous mountains, and as one can see the complete heights from sea-level, such figures as 3,500 feet mean far more than the 7,000 or even 10,000 feet heights of mountains situated far inland on plateaux in many countries. This is not all. The existence of Hinchinbrook Island can be regarded as part of the series of events which led to the existence of the Great Barrier Reefs, as will be seen from a perusal of the last section of this book. It was obviously a wild and magnificent stretch of Queensland which became cut off through the subsidence of the sea bottom (which has played a part, or so it is believed, in the formation of the outer coral reefs over the whole area).

This separation of Hinchinbrook as an island has resulted in the preservation of acres and acres of natural Australia, and so far as the land naturalist is concerned it is a marvellous reserve where wild life has been preserved amidst fascinating forests, which are difficult and probably dangerous for careless exploration.

The mountains are arranged in two series. The southern row has Mt. Bowen (the highest of all), 3,650 feet high, to the north, and then come Mt. Diamantina, 3,150 feet, four and a half miles south of it, and Mt. Straloch the southernmost, 3,020 feet high. North of Mt. Bowen in the northern range is Mt. Pitt, 2,350 feet high, and the island ends in a promontory with Cape Richards, 570 feet high.

The mountains are bare on their tops and sides, which are precipitous. The valleys are thick with most luxuriant vegetation, and streams with waterfalls are plentiful. The vista of those mountains rising from the jungle, reflected in the sea, is a sight never to be forgotten. Early morning is the time, when the sea is calm and the mountains are wreathed in mist. The western or channel coast of the island is somewhat flat and muddy with a thick covering of mangroves.

Hinchinbrook Channel, being narrow, is almost like a lake, especially since a bar guards the southern entrance. Dugong are found there still. It is a most impressive place and one still hears arguments as to whether the views from the channel or the outside (east) coast of the island are the best.

It is a grand thing that Hinchinbrook Island has been declared a national reserve, although one wonders how these reserves can be properly policed. But it is time that some of Australia's scientific societies organized land explorations on this wonderful continental island where twenty-two foot pythons are said still to hold their own, and orchids are only one item for enthusiastic botanists. Such explorations will need some planning, and will be only for those of excellent physique.

Earlier we mentioned the late Professor Wood Jones—a British scientist well known in both Melbourne and Adelaide as an anatomist. But he was also a charming writer and lecturer and an authority on corals and coral island formation—his work on the latter being carried out whilst a doctor on the Cocos Keeling Atoll. In one of the most delightful collections of non-scientific essays he tells a fine story of the advantages of some understanding of science when viewing nature's wonders. He impresses vividly in words the thoughts that must arise on seeing such scenic splendours as the Grand Canyon of Colorado if one has a little knowledge (even a very little) of geology, or the prospect of a grand sea coast to the man who can see and read in it also the vicissitudes of its history. In one of his stories he tells of the marvels of nature which we pass by almost every day without even realizing their existence. Now Wood Jones had made a visit to the Great Barrier Reef and presumably he had been greatly affected by the view of Hinchinbrook. In any case he wished to draw his story of the world's marvels to a telling climax, and he succeeded by bringing in a reference to the Hinchinbrook Channel. He described how he met an old sailor on the margin of a clay-pan filled with water in an otherwise desert region of Central Australia. The clay-pan was being visited daily by countless numbers of wonderfully coloured birds which fascinated both Wood Jones and the old sailor. But the latter confided to the scientist on his last night there that he had seen something which made the flocks of birds seem trivial and insignificant, and the words he used were, 'No one can sail through the Hinchinbrook Pass and not believe in God'. Wood Jones concluded his story with the paragraph: 'It would be worth considering if the Federal authorities could make it possible that the entire population of Australia should make annual passage of the Hinchinbrook Pass'.

Not far north of Hinchinbrook is Dunk Island, which was made famous by the late E. J. Banfield ('Beachcomber'), who lived there for twenty-five years, after he had received a fatal verdict from his doctor in England. He described his paradise in *My Tropic Isle*, and made it well known by details in other books. Dunk Island now has one of the well-equipped tourist centres of this part of Australia. We advise those who would really learn more of Dunk Island to read Banfield's works and to visit the place in the spirit of the man who wrote them.

The explorer with a launch might touch at one or more of a host of other islets—high or low ones—on his further way northward. We have referred to one or two of these already. Passing still northward, one finds islands and reefs, reefs exposed and reefs dangerously submerged, until Cape Flattery is reached and the outer barrier is only just twenty-five miles from the mainland. About twenty miles further north is the last continental island we shall mention. It also is famous in its history. It is Lizard Island, three miles long and two miles wide, with a peak 1,179 feet high. From the top of this island Captain Cook saw with surprise the submerged reeflets which dotted the sea all round his ship. The picture gave him a shock which caused him to seek the outer ocean through a gap in the barrier which has since then been known as Cook's Passage. He did not do too well outside, and came back again in a manner rather unorthodox, even for a sailing ship. (See page 74.)

Lizard Island, by the way, was used as a base by the British scientists, in 1929, for visits to the reefs of the outer barrier. It is very conveniently situated for such scientific explorations.

We have now reached the northern end of the Great Barrier Reef area. It is characterized by a relatively great area of shallow water in which are such an intricate scattering of small reeflets that it is probably the most difficult part of the whole region to navigate. It has, however, been a prolific region for *bêche-de-mer* and trochus-shell fisheries, in both of which pursuits the Japanese have taken their toll.

CAPTAIN COOK'S BARRIER REEF VOYAGE

For the sake of completeness, we now give a brief summary of some of the events which occurred in 1770 when Captain Cook made the first voyage of exploration along the Barrier Reef Channel.

Captain Cook, making the first known visit of any white man along the coast of Queensland, reached the latitude of those famous Queensland landmarks, the Glass House Mountains, on 17th May 1770. Influenced by their curious form he gave them their unique name. Without inquiry into the nature of the shore, but keeping 'two leagues' from land Cook continued sailing northward. He depended chiefly on soundings, sending on occasions a boat ahead of the ship. He named Sandy Cape on 20th May, and sailed slowly on. Five days later he was across the Tropic of Capricorn. He

71

mentions the occurrence of a few islands, but his account gives no indication of the coral archipelago he was nearing. We have tried to stress the reason for this in the foregoing section. Through keeping the coast of Australia in easy view as he sailed northward, Captain Cook entered the Great Barrier Reef Channel without seeing anything at all of the southern end of the Barrier Reef. The low islands and the reefs of the Capricorn and Bunker groups being about fifty miles from the Queensland coast were completely out of sight to the eastward.

Thus, instead of discovering the reefs of the outer barrier far to his right, Cook next met the group of continental islets called the Northumberland Isles, which are close to the land, and south of Mackay. He was now definitely inside the great channel without knowing it, and he did not strike anything like an entanglement of low coral islands and reefs until he was north of the latitude of Cairns.

He speaks of a landing on the mainland in search of fresh water and of climbing a hill to get a view of the islands off the coast, but even this would give no glimpse of the outer barrier, which is here rather broken up and at its greatest distance from the mainland. He continued northward, naming capes and promontories as he went and it is not surprising from the course taken that on 3rd June 1770, it being Whitsunday, he found himself in Whitsunday Passage, as he named it. It is strange, in some ways, that Cook had no words for the beauty of the scenery about him as he continued his northern passage, but on the whole the account of his voyage is not gilded by picturesque description. What was important to him was the fact that on several occasions he saw large columns of smoke on the mainland, and some people and canoes.

So Cook's account goes on.

He begins his next chapter by actually commenting on the fact that he had safely navigated hundreds of miles of dangerous coast without an accident, and that in consequence none of the names used for the various islands, promontories, and so on, suggest emotions of distress. Trouble was, however, to come. It is surprising that in spite of the course he took, there is little or no mention of coral in his log, because most of the islands passed have fringing reefs. The latitude where Cairns now stands was passed, and Cook bore on, but the outer barrier and its reefs were gradually closing in on his track. He seems to have become just a little suspicious of the waters about him, but not enough to prevent his sailing on after dark, under which conditions nothing would enable him to be aware early enough of a coral reef. And so on Sunday, 10th June 1770, a few minutes before 11 p.m., the ship struck fairly solidly on what is now called Endeavour Reef.

The crew, under instructions, threw overboard everything of any weight, from ballast to guns. There is no space here to describe the tragic position which Cook sets out at some length—the exhaustion of the men at the pumps, for example, for the ship leaked instead of rising with the tide after the ettisoning of the heavy stores. Eventually a procedure was adopted of hauling a sail covered with sheep's dung, oakum and wool under the ship's bottom by ropes. In this way the hole was covered. The *Endeavour* was floated and sailed in to an inlet on the coast which is now the harbour of Cooktown.

Here, whilst the ship was being repaired, the scientific staff (the famous Sir Joseph Banks, at that time only Mr Banks, was on board) made collections, and on one day Captain Cook climbed a hill to get a view of the sea. He saw with great concern: 'innumerable banks and shoals lying along the coast in every direction'.

He sent, therefore, the master of the ship in the pinnace to find a passage out to sea. The master returned with the information that the shoals consisted of coral and that on one of them he found some 'cockles of so enormous a size

73

that one of them was more than two men could eat'. This must have been the first mention of the giant clam. More explorations were made, both on land and in the channel, and Cook made another effort to view the seascape from a high hill. He writes, 'We were soon convinced that the danger of our situation was at least equal to our apprehensions; for in whatever direction we turned our eyes, we saw rocks and shoals without number and no passage out to sea, but through the winding channels beneath them, which could not be navigated without the last degree of difficulty and danger'.

It is amazing, the cheerfulness of these explorers, stranded on a shore which in terms of their kind of ship meant untold separation from their homeland. The *Endeavour* was only 370 tons, the size of a modern trawler.

On 4th August, eight weeks after he had been wrecked, Cook left what he had called the Endeavour River. By now he was fully aware of the amount of coral about him, but he rejected the suggestion that he should 'beat back the way we came'. His steering was therefore a matter of masthead vision and sending a boat ahead. This went on until he saw a group of islands and one of them a very high island—Lizard Island, to which we have already referred. Cook gave it the name because he said it abounded in lizards of a very large size.

From Lizard Island he saw for the first time the outer barrier. In his own words, 'I discovered a reef of rocks, lying between two and three leagues without any islands, and extending in a line N.W. and S.E. farther than I could see, upon which the sea broke in a dreadful surf; this, however, made me think there were no shoals beyond them, and I conceived hopes of getting without these, as I perceived several breaks or openings in the reef'.

Cook managed to find a navigable gap in the outer barrier and reached the open ocean, which he recognized by the

Pentecost Island viewed from Lindeman in the Whitsunday Group.

Hinchinbrook Island. —*Photo. Queensland Govt. Tourist Bureau.*

Green Island, Cairns.

Mutton Bird.

The settlement on Heron Island and a small part of the coral reef-flat at low water.

Looking down from Hayman on to the fringing reef which connects it with Arkhurst Island. —*Photo. Queensland Govt. Tourist Bureau.*

Mainland Islands, looking south along Long and Whitsunday Passages
from the Molle Group. —*Photo. Queensland Govt. Tourist Bureau.*

Approaching Heron Island from the sea.

The south-west point of Hayman Island with Langford Island in the distance. —*Photo. Isobel Bennett.*

East side of Pelsart Island, showing lagoons forming with broken coral. —*Photo. V. Serventy.*

Wreck Point, Pelsart Island, showing the nature of the old coral limestone of which the island mainly consists. —*Photo. V. Serventy.*

Part of a branch of a stagshorn coral *Acropora* (actual size), and (below) the same coral magnified, showing the cups for the individual polyps. —*Photos. Gwen Burns.*

large sea rolling. He says the change of situation was now visible on every countenance (meaning that cheerfulness was once more registered). This, however, was premature, for within three days he found himself in the truly horrible position of drifting back on the outer barrier he had been so glad to leave behind. He also found that a current like a mill-stream ran through the gaps in the reef, in or out according to the tide. In fact it was through the flood tide which carried the ship 'as in a torrent' through one of these gaps that he succeeded in reaching the inside of the channel once again. 'And now such is the vicissitude of life, we thought ourselves happy in having regained a situation which but two days before it was the utmost object of our hope to quit.' He called the opening the Providential Channel, and decided from then on to keep once more within close range of the mainland coast.

And so continuing onward Cook reached Cape York and the Torres Strait and eventually rounded the northern point of Queensland. But notwithstanding all that had happened, he and his crew left Australia without realizing the existence of twelve hundred miles of coral reefs forming an outer barrier to the channel he had navigated, and the greatest coral reef development in the world's seas.

3

The Coral Islands of
Western Australia

WESTERN AUSTRALIA has no barrier reef, but it has some exceedingly interesting coral islands. This is unusual, because the west coasts of all the great continents are generally without coral reefs. Warm ocean currents are driven westward across the oceans, and so impinge on the east coasts of continents, washing the shores of Florida, Queensland and Torres Strait, the Red Sea and other African localities, whilst cold water upwells on the west. Australia is thus rather exceptional in its western reefs, but the islands of which I am going to speak are more exceptional still because they are so far south of the Equator. Their existence is quite unexpected since, more or less in accordance with the rule just mentioned, there is practically no coral reef development on the mainland shores at the same latitude. Their extraordinary history puts the final touch to their interest for us.

The Abrolhos Islands, also called Houtman Abrolhos, became known to Europeans long before the Great Barrier Reef. They are situated well out to sea, about forty-five miles off Geraldton, in latitude approximately 28° 40′ S. Fringing coral reefs occur here and there along the north-west coast of Australia, but few people other than fishermen and stray zoologists know much of them.

84

The Abrolhos Islands are unlike the islands of the Barrier Reef region. Although entirely composed of coral or coral sand, and rock which is part coral and part other limy remains of animals and plants, the larger islands are higher and different in other characteristics from any coral islands of the Barrier Reef Channel. The story of their origin is a matter more for the scientist than for the general reader.

If one glances at a map one will see that the Abrolhos Group consists of a series of islets or sub-groups in a line. North Island consists of coral limestone rock and sand which rises as dunes to a height of forty-two feet. It is surrounded by fringing reefs. The island bears a few shrubs and is not very attractive.

The Wallabi Isles form the largest and most interesting sub-group of the Abrolhos. The island nearest North Island is East Wallabi Island. It actually reaches a height of forty or fifty feet, and much of it is old coral rock (with old shells in it). This island is connected with West Wallabi Island at low water by a reef-flat of coral and both islands have fringing reefs with very beautiful coral growths.

Part of the surface of these islands is sand which is burrowed everywhere by the mutton-birds, the same species as that which nests on Heron Island and other islets off the Queensland coast. Here, as there, walking over the ground is difficult and exciting, as one leg or the other suddenly goes through to the thigh. Once upon a time much of the surface of the Abrolhos Islands were covered with a rich deposit of guano—but most has been removed and sold. Its existence is proof of the outstanding part these islands have played as the nesting places of sea-birds.

The Wallabi Islands are remarkable for the presence of certain animals which properly belong to the mainland and are certainly not the proper denizens of coral islands. The most striking of these are wallabies, which are so numerous

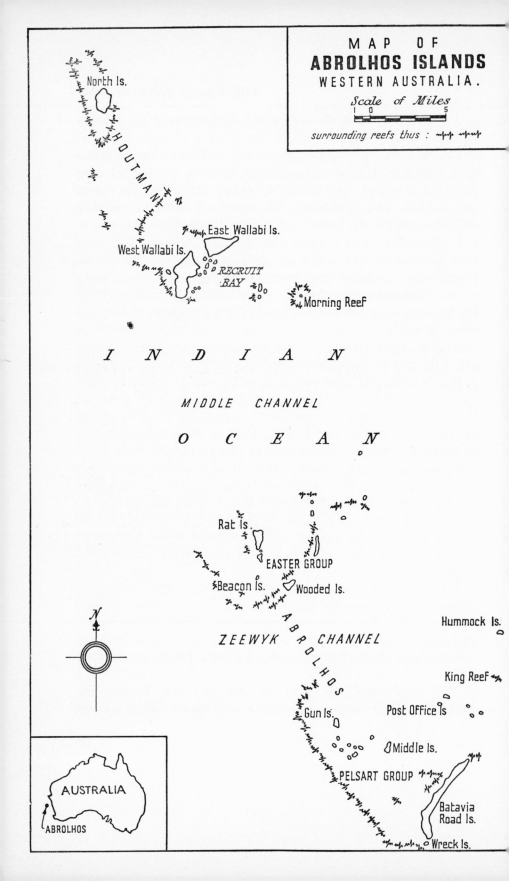

MAP OF
ABROLHOS ISLANDS
WESTERN AUSTRALIA.

Scale of Miles

1   0   5

surrounding reefs thus :

North Is.

H O U T M A N

East Wallabi Is.

West Wallabi Is.

RECRUIT BAY

Morning Reef

I N D I A N

MIDDLE CHANNEL

O C E A N

Rat Is.

EASTER GROUP

Beacon Is.   Wooded Is.

Hummock Is.

N

ZEEWYK   CHANNEL

A B R O L H O S

King Reef

Gun Is.

Post Office Is

Middle Is.

PELSART GROUP

Batavia Road Is.

Wreck Is.

AUSTRALIA

ABROLHOS

that the writer and his lugger captain chased them with sticks and caught several alive.

About fourteen miles south of the Wallabi Island Group is the Easter Group, separated from it by a channel with depths averaging twenty-five to thirty fathoms. This sub-group looks rather different from the Wallabi Group and there is a reef surrounding a lagoon with the largest island of the sub-group (Rat Island) inside it. It looks as if it were well on the way to being an atoll, but the depths on the outside are not more than twenty-five fathoms and the story of its formation is probably quite different from that of the true atolls of the open ocean. There are some other small islets in the lagoon and many reefs awash at low tide. The encircling reefs which form a breakwater against the ocean swell are two to five miles away from the little central islands.

South of Easter Group and separated from it by a narrow channel roughly twenty-five to thirty fathoms deep is the Pelsart Group, which is the most famous of all. This group of islets and reefs looks exactly like an atoll, a lagoon surrounded by reefs of which one is higher (about eight feet), forming land on the eastern side. It is however, not a true atoll if we define that as having considerable ocean depths on the outside. The western reef looks, however, very much like part of an atoll rim and the Indian Ocean swell breaks full on it in the manner typical of oceanic atolls. One looks for beautiful living corals on the lee side, in the lagoon, and finds them.

All these island groups provide excellent sheltered spots with good anchorage for launches, and the author has camped on them all. One must steer one's ship about these islands and their lagoons when the sun is high, and with a 'lookout' on constant watch for submerged coral. There is no other way.

The origin and the form of the Abrolhos Islands are problems which we cannot enter into here. What we see today is the consequence of coral growth, of changes in sea level, of erosion by sea and by the atmosphere; in fact, the result of a cycle which may have taken hundreds of thousands of years. The existence of the wallabies, snakes, lizards, and other creatures tells, however, of an ancient connection with the mainland of Western Australia, so the low islands of coral have a somewhat more complex history than might at first be imagined and one that is different from that of the low coral islands of the Barrier Reef.

One cannot describe the islands themselves as beautiful. They are more or less covered with dull-coloured shrubs, the highest plants being mangroves which are found only in some sheltered nooks on the lagoon side. But there is certainly a fascination in camping on these shores. And the coral growths are excellent; even Saville Kent* said that he had seen nothing finer on the Barrier Reef. Today the islands are a well-established fishing centre, and over 3,500,000 lb. of lobsters were caught in 1960.

This description cannot be left without a brief mention of the extraordinary picture of bird life presented by some of the islands at one season at least of the year. One ornithologist, A. J. Campbell, went so far as to say that probably the Abrolhos 'form the greatest rookery for sea-birds in Australia and by reason of their geographical position in the subtropics, perhaps afford suitable breeding grounds for a greater number of species than any other distinct or limited spot in the world'.

When I was there on one occasion a great area of West Wallabi Island was literally covered with the nests of Pacific gulls, caspian terns, silver gulls and pied cormorants. As we walked between them the cormorants left first, being most

---

*W. Saville Kent, an Englishman who was Commissioner of Fisheries to the Government of Western Australia during the last years of the nineteenth century, is best known for his magnificent monograph which was published in England in 1893 and possibly now is available only in official libraries: *The Great Barrier Reef of Australia: Its Products and Potentialities.*

shy, and before the gulls were frightened they actually attacked the eggs of the cormorants, making quick gluttons of themselves on yolk or chicks before flying off. In other places noddy terns were abundant. Most curious of all, however, were the more rare lesser noddy terns, which make nests of seaweed well up on the branches of the mangroves. In fact the mangrove swamp on Wooded Island, as a result of these nesting birds, looked like a scene devised by surrealists.

However, this is not all. What the Abrolhos may lack in beauty on land they make up in historical interest, and something of this must certainly be added to our story. In fact, no Australian should grow up without having heard about it.

The Abrolhos Islands were certainly visited by a Dutchman, F. Houtman, in 1617, at the beginning of what Jeans has called the century of genius, but it has been suggested that this lonely outpost of Australia had already been discovered by a Portuguese navigator, Meneses, in 1527 (nearly a century before Houtman passed it); it is known with certainty that in 1526-7 Meneses discovered part of the northwest coast of New Guinea. Columbus, Vasco da Gama and Magellan had revealed that there was another world to be developed. Galileo was startling the intellectual world. The Dutch were very quick to exploit new results of sea exploration and soon were established in what was until recent years the Netherlands East Indies, with headquarters in Batavia.

The Dutch pilots responsible for navigation had discovered that the best way to reach Batavia after rounding the Cape of Good Hope was to keep on, due eastward, until a certain distance had been traversed. Then, if they changed course north-east, they would more quickly reach their destination, provided always that they did not get blown too far east to begin with. This brought the danger of striking an outpost of Australia—the reefs of the Abrolhos. Too

89

many of their ships did strike the Abrolhos, or the coast of Western Australia thereabouts, but the most famous wreck was that in 1629 of an emigrant ship, the *Batavia*, under Captain Pelsaert. The staggering series of events which followed was told later by Pelsaert himself in a story which became one of the world's first best-sellers and thrillers.

The *Batavia* left Holland in October 1628 with an exceedingly mixed crowd on board, one of whom, the supercargo Jerome Cornelius, had already planned to seize the ship when an opportunity arose, and sail the seas as a pirate. The opportunity never occured on the high seas, but in June 1629 early in the morning the *Batavia* crashed on a coral reef of the Abrolhos Islands. (Until recently it was thought that the wreck occurred in the Pelsart Group of islands, but it is now believed to have taken place on the southern end of Noon Reef in the Wallabi Group.)

Pelsaert managed to get practically all his people ashore (the passengers included women and children), but what followed could scarcely be exceeded by the author of any adventure story of fiction. It is a tale of castaways short of food and starved of water, of wholesale murder, and of Cornelius setting himself up as the tyrant governor of a barren island and in fact decking himself out with the scarlet and gold robes intended for state occasions in Batavia. It is also a story of heroism on the part of a few, and of an amazing journey by Pelsaert in an open boat to bring help from Batavia, two thousand miles away, along the inhospitable and unknown coast of north-western Australia.

The survivors had reached and occupied more than one of the islands of the Pelsart Group, which was fortunate for those decent men who planned for a rescue. By almost a miracle Pelsaert returned with a ship, and the mutineers met their just fate.

The story of the Abrolhos was read by the peoples of Europe three hundred years ago, and before Australia meant

Turbinaria coral skeleton.

Turbinaria coral with living polyps expanded at night.
—*Photo. T. A. Stephenson.*

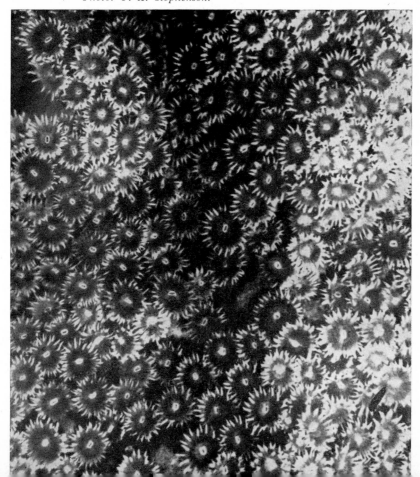

Diagrammatic internal and external views of an anemone. —(*W. J. Dakin del.*)

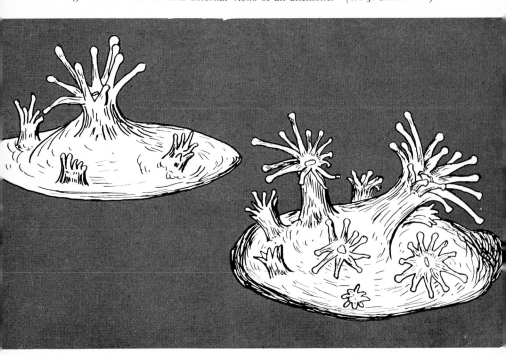

Diagram showing the growth and budding of a very young coral *(Pocillopora)*, artificially reared (two weeks and five days' growth).

Opposite, above: One of the staghorn corals *(Acropora s*
and a specimen of the large sea star *(Pentaceraster austra*
Below: Two stromb shells *(Strombus* spp.), and a pincushion
(Culcita novae-guineae). Photos. Isobel Ben

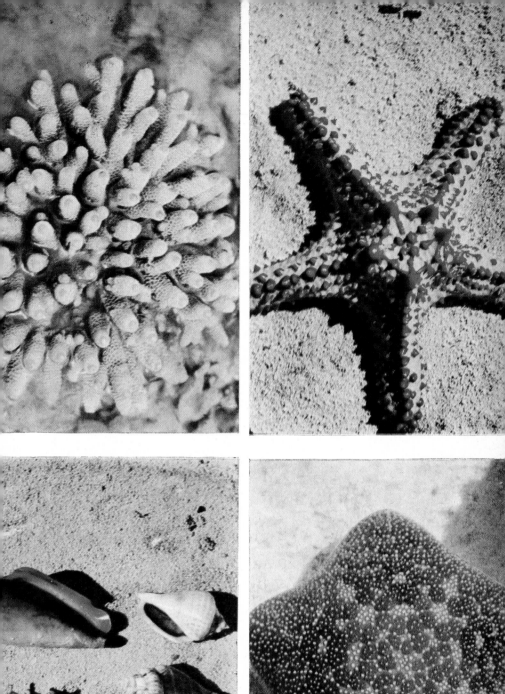

anything at all to the white nations of the world. And in his account of what happened Pelsaert gives a description of the wallaby, still so abundant in the Wallabi Island group. Obviously the curious animal had made an impression despite the horrors of the tragedy. It was the first description of any member of the kangaroo tribe to reach civilization, and in it Pelsaert made an amazing mistake which for some reason has recurred thousands of times in the country pubs and stations of Australia during the last century. He actually stated that the young of the animal grew out of the nipples of the mother!

Possibly only those who live in Australia will realize what it means to refer to this as an absurdity. Only the country folk of Australia know of the hot arguments which have been waged concerning the birth of the kangaroo. (Since the kangaroo is a marsupial and the young embryo is less than an inch long at birth, it was very difficult to convince the uneducated stockmen of the real facts, and arguments often ended as battles royal.)

So the discovery of the Abrolhos Islands is a story of bloodshed and piracy, of the first white settlement on Australia (even if compulsory and temporary), and of the kangaroo tribe. Today a visit to the islands is a simple matter of hiring a launch from Geraldton, or making a trip with one of the fishing fleets. In 1913 and 1915, on my two explorations, I had to hire pearling luggers and their crews. A sailing vessel without engine is, however, not exactly the craft for this region where navigation with any sort of ship is restricted to the hours when the sun is high, and someone up the mast can look ahead and detect the hidden masses of coral, which do not grow up above sea-level, but are numerous enough at depths just dangerous for small fishing vessels of light draught. I shall never forget the difficulty of that navigation and the long journey (for our craft) down the Pelsart Lagoon.

4

Some Common Corals and Related Animals

As we have already mentioned, the zoologist is faced with something of a problem when he tries to explain the coral animal to the average person. In fact, I often wonder whether it is possible so to describe a coral, or a sponge, or any other of the world's lowly animals, that the ordinary reader will appreciate the nature of their bodies. For the same reason I always wonder, as a naturalist, what the visitor to coral islands really thinks of the so-called coral that he sees. Much of it, if not most, consists of rough and well-born blocks of a white stony nature (it is limestone, in fact) thrown up by the waves on the shore.

Let us start off with the fact that this limy product of the tropical seas, whether it be fresh and beautiful, worn and shapeless, solid or delicately branched, is nothing but the remains of the creatures which were once coral—that is to say, live coral. A piece of this so-called coral could be more appropriately termed the skeleton. Let us make another comparison and say that it bears the same relation to the live animal as the shell of a snail to the creeping creature which makes it. Both are limy secretions from the outside of the animal, but the coral animal is a lowly jelly-like creature which simply sits over the hard limy structure it has made,

94

whereas the snail (although you might not think so) is a much more highly organized animal with head and eyes and heart and nervous system, and is capable of wandering about and seeking its food. We have provided several photographs of the coral skeleton and one cannot deny that it is beautiful, but this applies more especially when it is fresh and clean and not dust-covered and broken on somebody's mantelpiece.

This skeleton is very rarely the remains of a single individual. It is usually the hard secretion of a *group* of coral animals, all of which originated from *one* individual, which itself was the product of a fertilized egg. So we must learn at the outset that coral reproduces itself in two ways—sexually by eggs and sperms, and asexually by budding almost like a plant, so that vast colonies (as they are called) may result from one individual.

There are some coral animals which remain single individuals, solitary corals, they are called, and they are relatively large—a few inches across—when compared with the usual size. The mushroom coral is an example. You may get an idea of the size of the individuals by glancing at a piece of coral skeleton. You will notice that its surface is covered with holes or depressions generally only a fraction of an inch across. Each depression represents the place where one coral polyp was seated. 'Polyp' is the zoological term for the small coral animal.

We are all so used to the higher animals having legs and walking about, having hearts and brains, blood vessels and bowels, that it is no wonder we show such ignorance of the more numerous tiny creatures, which often prove very dangerous to human life. Even a crab has all the parts we have just named, and other organs which are represented in the human body, although by very different-looking structures. A crab's leg is distinctly different from a dog's leg or a human leg to begin with, and a crab's eye is nothing like a human eye or even a frog's eye. But a coral polyp is so different from an insect or a crustacean or any of the higher animals that it is nothing like the creatures people usually regard as animals.

You must forget then the human body, or the body of a fish, when you try to learn about coral, and you must certainly banish from your mind the idea of a coral being an insect. Insects are characterized by having wings and six legs. Flies and ants are insects and almost the entire group (the biggest in the animal kingdom) 'detests' sea water above all things.

One of the first things a student learns about animals is that some grow fixed or attached to other objects and actually branch like plants. But if a creature has a mouth, and uses it to swallow living or dead organic matter which it *must have as food*, you can bet on its being an animal, no matter what it looks like.

Fortunately, anyone who really wants to know what a coral animal is like can find out without too much difficulty, for it has a close relative which is common on practically all the seashores of the world. This is the sea-anemone, of which there are many different kinds, typically of attractive colours, and most of them averaging an inch or two in diameter. Perhaps the easiest way of explaining the exact nature of a coral polyp is to describe its larger relative, but we must remember that the anemone has no limy skeleton like the corals; and instead of finding anemones in united groups which, as we have just indicated, is characteristic of our reef corals, we discover that they exist mostly as separate individuals. So, on the whole, the anemone is simpler than the coral, but only in these few respects.

A sea-anemone, described in the simplest terms, has a column-shaped body with a circular disc at the top. Round the margins of this disc are circlets of tentacles (the number varies according to the species, but is often a multiple of six), and in the middle of the disc is one opening, the mouth. The creature looks as if made of jelly (it is in fact closely related to the jellyfish), and this characteristic is very obvious in the case of those species which live relatively high up on rocky shores; when the tide goes out and they are exposed to the air the anemones contract until they are mere blobs of jelly, and the tentacles are withdrawn out of sight.

This character of contracting to a shapeless mass should be kept in mind, because the coral animals are exactly the same as anemones in this respect and when they contract, which they do, not only if taken out of the water (or exposed to air by the tide leaving them above sea-level for an hour or so) but usually during the daytime, the living body can scarcely be seen at all, the flesh being of such a delicate nature. There is in consequence a tremendous difference between a fully expanded anemone (or coral polyp) with all its beautiful tentacles widespread like the petals of a flower, and one that is shut up and contracted almost to nothingness.

And now you will surely ask how this simple animal catches its food since (being attached to the rocks by the base of its column) it does not move after it, and since it has no eyes to see. It depends on particles of suitable organic matter, or on animals floating or swimming about, colliding by accident with the tentacles. This explains why moving water is best. There is more chance of minute animals being carried up against the tentacles. Those tentacles which look so beautiful are armed with stinging cells which shoot out microscopic threads as do the jellyfish so well known to surfers.

Whether or not corals are purely carnivorous is still today the subject of controversy. One sideline arising out of the development of the atom bomb has been the amazing amount of research during the last decade among the coral reefs of the Pacific and Atlantic. New scientific tools such as radioactive isotopes and the electron microscope have been used by teams of workers particularly in the Marshall Islands* and the West Indies.†

If a tiny animal drifts against one or two of the tentacles of the anemone or coral polyp it becomes stunned and is held. It has been stung—pierced by a hundred or more thread cells. Then one sees other tentacles bending over to lend their aid. Even an active little fish may be captured in this way. Finally the tentacles pass their capture to the centre, and there it goes through the mouth and so to the inside. Do not forget that, with one or two exceptions, the coral animals expand and extend their tentacles *at night* in readiness for catching food. During the day the living body is so contracted that the tentacles may not be visible at all. Even the living tissue can scarcely be distinguished. This fits in rather well with the conditions in the sea, because at night there are far more microscopic animals floating and swimming in the surface water. They go downwards in daylight. This is unfortunate, however, for the tourist, who in consequence rarely sees the corals at their very best.

We have said nothing about the inside of an anemone because this is not a treatise on anatomy, but one or two sentences will be sufficient to show how different both the anemone and coral are from most of the better-known animals. Even the garden earthworm has stomach and intestine, but the body of an anemone consists practically only of a wall of living tissue and one space inside it. The mouth leads into this space and so the interior of the animal will actually contain some sea-water. Of course this simple anatomical arrangement leads to a distinct peculiarity. The food which goes through the mouth and reaches that one central space of the body is digested there, but anything

---

*Odum & Odum:Trophic structure and productivity of a windward coral reef community on Eniwetok Atoll. *Ecol. Monog.* 25 (3), 1955.

†Goreau: Problems of growth and calcium deposition on coral reefs. *Endeavour* 20 (77), 1961.

which is left undigested must go out by the same way it came in, via the mouth. The procedure is as simple as the structure of the body itself.

The outside surface of the body, like our own skin, does service as a protective covering, and it can feel too, but this does not exhaust the possibilities of its living cells because the skin of the tentacles can obviously taste and distinguish between what is good to eat and what is not. Moreover, it bears the stinging and attachment cells. The inside tissue of the body, which lines the body space, likewise performs several duties. The digestive juices are manufactured by it, and it also bears the reproductive organs.

To be accurate and complete we should, however, describe one other detail of the internal space. I had a friend who devoted his life to the collection of rare books. For many years he was able to find room for them at home, but only because, having covered all the walls of his sitting room with bookshelves, he proceeded to build bookcases which projected from the walls into the room. In this way he increased the area of shelving enormously even if he spoilt his long-suffering wife's best entertaining room. Now, the inner wall of the anemone also projects into the central space in the form of a regular series of vertical partitions (called mesenteries) as you can see in the diagram (page 92). We can be allowed to assume that, like my book-loving friend's arrangement, this feature of the anemone is to increase the digestive area and leave room for supports for ovaries, etc.

In the coral polyp the tissues perform an additional function—the secretion of the limy skeleton. This calcareous material is secreted in the partitions inside the polyp, in its base, and also between each individual in a colony. The intricate patterns formed by the different species are to a great extent responsible for the exquisite beauty of the coral skeleton.

The complex mechanism whereby this tiny creature

absorbs the calcium salts from the sea water and deposits them as skeleton has been the subject of much research and experiment, and is still only partially understood.

Sexual reproduction in the corals (we might as well definitely refer to corals now in this respect, for they have the same structural organization as the anemone) is such that the mesenteries of any one individual bear either ovaries, or testes, or both. The animal is thus male, female, or hermaphrodite. (In the latter case it has been shown that does not function as male and female at the same time.)

The sperms are released and float out into the sea water in their due season. Many will, of course, be lost; some will be drawn through the mouth into the body-space of other nearby individuals, and that is. how the eggs become fertilized. The eggs develop into tiny larvae called planulae which leave the parent and for a few days swim or drift until they settle down and commence their attached life. In the case of the corals, the breeding season may be limited or very prolonged, extending over several months. Some of them, like other sea animals, spawn at certain phases of the moon, a phenomenon still not properly understood.

At the earliest stage in its life, a coral is probably about a sixteenth of an inch long. It swims about for a few days probably rarely exceeding a week, and is more or less at the mercy of any currents. Then it settles down and quickly grows a set of tentacles. In no less than two weeks and five days, one of these young, grown in a glass dish in the course of some very beautiful studies made by Professor T. A. Stephenson at Low Isles on the Barrier Reef, had already produced four buds surrounding the original polyp. This was a coral species in which these little individuals were only about a sixteenth of an inch in height. And so by budding, a host of individuals, each covering its coral skeleton, comes into existence, and this may go on until a massive colony yards across has resulted. One example has been cited where,

A fine specimen of brain coral exposed at low water, Whitsunday Island.

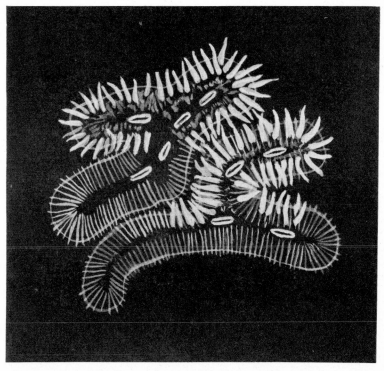

Diagram of small part of a brain coral showing how several mouths lie in a line surrounded by one series of tentacles. Part of the sketch shows skeleton surface only, and part is covered by living tissue.
—(*W. J. Dakin del.*)

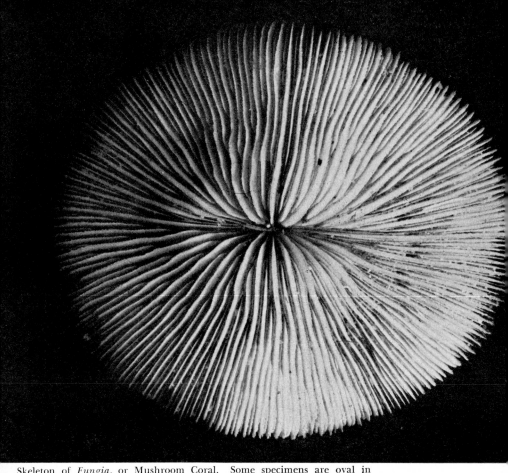

Skeleton of *Fungia,* or Mushroom Coral.   Some specimens are oval in shape and a foot or more in length.

Three mushroom corals in life.   These three corals are in different states of expansion.   One is nearly contracted and shows the mouth very clearly in the centre, and traces of the skeleton.   In the other two the tentacles are well expanded.   *—Photo. Saville Kent.*

Coral *(Pocillopora)* with cup-shaped formation caused by the gall-forming crab, *Haplocarcinus marsupialis.* (Below) *Acrhelia* is one of the most beautiful coral skeletons.

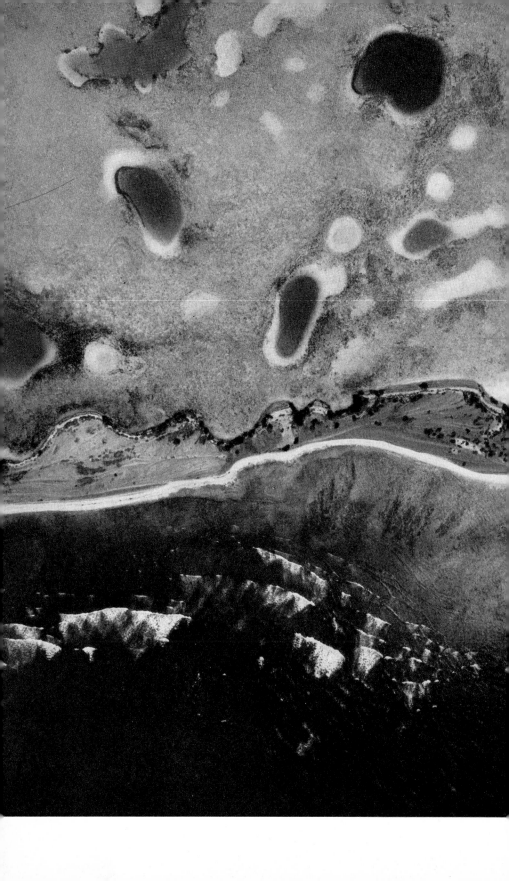

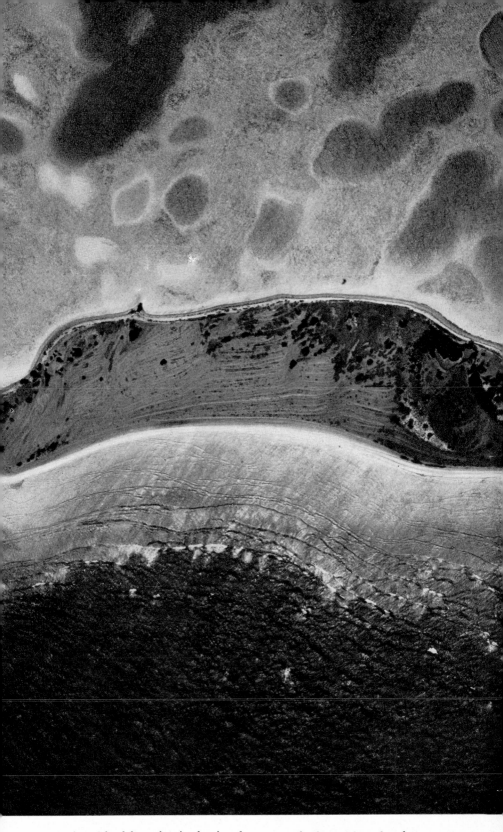

Pelsart Island from the air, showing the pattern of submerged coral reefs.
—*Photo. R.A.A.F. Official.*

Soft corals, *Lobophyton* (above) and *Sinularia* (below).

One of the soft corals taken under water with the polyps partly extended. (*Sarcophyton*)—*Photo. Frank McNeill.*

The giant anemone of the Great Barrier Reef (*Stoichactis kenti*).

—*Photo. Frank McNeill.*

Heap of starfish *(Protoreaster nodosus)* collected on the shore of a Great Barrier Reef Island. In summer these starfish may be found in hundreds on the shore at low water. *(Turn photo. to right.)*

after 1,030 days, a new anchor chain which had been lying at the bottom of a harbour for that period in Fiji, carried one colony with 25,470 polyps. (It was only about one pound in weight.)

But the types of budding are probably as varied in corals as in plants, and we cannot answer all the questions which are likely to be put by anyone who has become enthusiastic after walking over a coral reef at low tide. How long do the individuals live in such a coral colony? One scientist has suggested that the coral polyp 'is a living thing which knows no time of youthful vigour, no waxing to a period of adult life, no waning to senility—it knows no age—it practically knows no natural death'. Who knows?

It is to their curious method of growth and of producing new individuals that the so-called 'brain corals' owe the nature of their coral skeletons. In order to appreciate this, however, let us glance more carefully at the limy skeleton, which is for us the essential difference between an anemone and a coral.

As we have already indicated, each little limy cup in which an individual coral polyp sits not only consists of a base and cup-like part, but has a number of radiating partitions (septa) projecting inwards. It is these partitions which often give the delicate beauty of the coral skeleton. In fact it is the radiating partitions which give all the character to the mushroom coral (*Fungia*). They are of course much more striking in the case of corals with large individuals like those seen in the photographs of *Fungia* and *Turbinaria*, but a pocket lens will show they are always present. (One might naturally expect that they would correspond to the fleshy mesenteries of the anemones, but the coral polyp has these too.) Without the limy partitions the brain corals would never have got such a name, whilst *Fungia* would be totally different.

In the case of very many kinds of coral which we find producing branched or massive growths on our reefs, the surface of the limy skeleton seems divided up into depressions or apertures which are regularly arranged and of uniform size, each of which we have assumed to be the site of one coral polyp. The surface of brain coral is quite unlike this. It has long 'valleys' on it which turn after a short course like the depressions on the surface of the human brain. Each valley has its own set of little partitions. Surely this does not mean that each little valley represents the site of one coral polyp of very flattened shape?

The answer comes when a piece of brain coral is examined with the tentacles and living parts expanded at night. Then we notice that whilst there is one set of tentacles round each valley, there are several mouths in a line. During growth and production of new individuals, there have been many incomplete divisions. The strange effect on the skeleton is simply due to an unusual type of growth. (See page 101.)

There is one more question at least which I am sure some observant visitor will ask when he sees a huge block of some sort of massive coral, and that is, 'Please tell me how it comes that all that great thickness of limestone is the skeleton of the thin layer of living polyps on top. Is it still part of their skeleton and alive or is it just dead? It is so very different from the skeleton of a frog or a man which is inside and stops growing'.

Here is the answer. That great block of living and dead coral started as we have seen as part of one very small individual. This creature budded others or divided again and again until there was a little group of polyps. But these little individuals kept on secreting hard limy stone beneath them just as you might thicken the bottom of a teacup as you built up its rim, whilst other new cups were made side by side. Or you might just save material and make a platform across each cup cutting off the bottom part altogether, and you could repeat this many times so as to keep the open cavity always about the same depth.

So the coral skeleton spreads underneath the new individuals horizontally, but they gradually cut themselves off
from what was once the lower part of the skeleton as it grows
in thickness. The living creatures may thus remain as a thin
living layer on the surface of a great block of what is
practically dead stone.

And now in conclusion we must consider the special conditions in the sea which favour or restrict coral reef growth.
This is most important for any understanding of the puzzles
of coral reefs, as we stressed earlier. The reef corals are
rather particular in their requirements. They will not live
except in the tropics because the sea must never be colder
than 70° F. for their best development. Still more important
is the fact that they will not live in deep water. The sea
bottom must be less than 180 feet deep (which is really very
shallow indeed) if reefs are to grow properly. This is now
believed to be due to the fact that corals need light, and
sunlight is quickly absorbed as it passes down through sea
water.

For many years now it has been known that reef-building
corals need sunlight because (like the great clams) they have
thousands and thousands of microscopic plants living right
within their tissues. And these plants, like all our familiar
green plants on land, need sunlight. Removed from the
corals, the tiny plants, of which there are two different types,
will not survive. Their advantage to the reef-building corals
has been the subject of a very great deal of research. A series
of studies carried out over thirty years ago at Low Isles on
the Barrier Reef seemed to indicate that small coral colonies
could grow quite well without the tiny plants and that the
coral polyps obtained their foods solely from the microscopic animals floating about in the surrounding water. But
recent research has shown that when it comes to the great
bulk of a larger living reef the role of the microscopic plants
is of great significance to the survival and rapid growth of

the large reef-building corals. It had been assumed for nearly a hundred years that coral animals were easily killed by rain or fresh water of rivers, and that sand and mud were both very deleterious. But there is some doubt about the potency of these factors in causing the death of coral. We must recognize quite definitely that different kinds of coral are adapted to living under different conditions. Some cannot stand exposure to air and uncovering by the tide, whilst others have become well adapted to survival at intertidal levels. Thus we can see them easily, and appreciate some of their beauty when the tide goes out.

SOME CORAL SPECIES

The most abundant coral type in the sheltered and shallow parts of the lagoons visited by tourists is the stagshorn coral (*Acropora*). There are very many species of this genus, and actually the most common branching form does not look like a stag's horn. There is another very common species of *Acropora* in which a great many little vertical shoots arise from a horizontal expansion. It cannot be missed in the lagoon pools. I once walked on one of these horizontal expansions thinking the whole was strong enough to support me. The result was disastrous, for the pool was deep, and coral branches scratched off a considerable part of my skin.

The large brain corals have already been referred to and are easily recognized. The same can be said of the very different-looking coral skeleton of *Fungia*, the mushroom coral to which we have already referred. But *Fungia* is so numerous and so extraordinary in many ways that we cannot leave it without a little more of its story. The specimens of *Fungia* are found loose, and each, as we have pointed out, belongs to one animal which is unusually large for a coral—

maybe three or four inches or more across. The reason for the name is obvious, it looks like a mushroom (with no stalk) lying upside down. (Pages 102 and 151.)

But *Fungia* starts off by growing with a skeleton like a cup on a stalk, and attached to a stone or rock. (This originated from an egg and fertilization.) Gradually the cup widens into a mushroom-like disc, and then, as if too big, it comes off the stalk, falls down and proceeds to grow as one solitary big coral animal with skeleton. The extraordinary thing, however, is that the stalk which was left goes on producing another head with mushroom-like skeleton, and in due course this also breaks off and goes away to live on its own. How long this can continue no one knows.

We might add *Montipora* to the above list. The skeleton is branched or has the form of flat surfaces rolled in a scroll-like form and dotted with rather small cavities for its small-sized polyps.

We have given a picture of two *Turbinarias* to show the differences between the skeleton alone and the complete living and extended animal. Each individual here is of a moderately large size, between a quarter and a third of an inch in diameter.

I hope this description with the pictures will explain what a visitor sees when he looks down into the water at a living patch of coral by day. He should now understand why he does not (except in the case of very few species) see the mouths surrounded by tentacles even when he has a large type like the mushroom coral before him. Each individual of the stagshorn coral is, however, so small that one would not expect to see the tentacles even at night when they are expanded unless special magnifying equipment were available and proper means of illumination.

It is practically useless giving a list of other corals without pictures, and even with pictures an inexperienced person would find it impossible to identify them because they have a trick of growing differently according to the physical conditions of the place where they are found living.

Some curio-hunters break off pieces of coral and bring them back to shore. This is in many places illegal. In any case what happens? The polyps contract. Very soon they die, and the piece of coral becomes an ugly stinking mess. Eventually, bleached white by the sun and with all the living tissue dried up and decayed, even the piece of coral skeleton may still have beauty. But who wants to see this collecting dirt on a distant mantelpiece whilst the beautiful living reefs become distorted and destroyed by careless collectors?

Let me conclude this by reminding the reader once again that, although it is impossible to have coral reefs without coral, the coral reefs (and islands) are never completely composed of coral. Far from it. A surprising amount of material consists of the limy remains of microscopic animals such as foraminifera shells, of worm-tubes, soft corals, and mollusc shells, and the starfish and its relatives. But perhaps most surprising of all is the fact that coral reefs owe so much of their existence to the plant kingdom—both for their healthy growth and for their stability. We have already mentioned that the surface of the outer edge of a reef and often the reef crest are encrusted with pink limy seaweed. But one cannot stress too much the importance of the part played by these calcareous algae in cementing and binding together dead shells, worm-tubes and all the broken branching corals and giving permanence and solidarity to the reef as a whole.

THE SOFT CORALS

No visitor who fossicks about the coral flats at low tide can fail to be puzzled by large fleshy or leathery growths with lots of rounded lobes. They are not exactly beautiful when exposed to the air (and view) at times of low water.

Their colour may be an olive green with a tendency to dull yellow, or some other variant such as grey. I suppose given a guess the stranger would say they were some kind of seaweed. Actually they are very close relations of the corals and if examined under the proper conditions under water, hundreds of exceedingly beautiful little polyps will be seen, each one with its column and disc but always with eight tentacles round the mouth. The tentacles are an infallible clue to their identity, for the number is always eight and each tentacle is fringed with lovely little branches on its sides. These creatures are known as soft corals. Like the true corals they are also found on the seashores of colder parts of the world, although more numerous by far in the tropics.

The most easily recognized soft corals on the Great Barrier Reef flats are *Lobophyton* and *Sarcophyton*. There are other very different members of this class of animal too, whose skeletons should delight the visitor, namely, organ-pipe coral and the blue coral called *Heliopora*. (Both of these have rigid limy skeletons.)

ORGAN-PIPE CORAL

We suggest that the untrained visitor to coral shores should try to get a guide who can demonstrate some of the creatures we have touched upon. Ask someone to show you organ-pipe coral (*Tubipora musica*) alive, with its green polyps expanded, and see the red skeleton appear visible when it is touched, causing the green flesh to contract. You will then understand how most of us are as men blind to the hidden glories of nature if we only go 'fossicking' in the ordinary fashion.

THE ANEMONES

We have described a general type of anemone with a diagrammatic illustration that is not unlike some of the anemones

115

common on the southern Australian coasts. There are many species of anemones on the coral reefs and they are all beautiful, often with colours which are unusual for animal life. But when the Great Barrier Reef is mentioned, one species of anemone stands out above all others. It is the large anemone, *Stoichactis kenti*, which is not only common but counts among the world's largest anemones. The disc bears hundreds of tentacles, and as if to find room for them, its surface is folded. Its colour varies, and some specimens have tentacles of a dark blue, brownish-purple, or dark green hue. Another larger and very beautiful anemone living among dead coral boulders is the pale fawn-coloured *Physobrachia ramsayi*.

Both these anemones often shelter small fish and prawns which are very peculiarly adapted to the anemone, so that one can speak of them as messmates. Nature has contrived that these creatures can live together and touch each other without the stinging and capture by the anemone which follows such contacts made by other species. The whole business is another of nature's most fascinating puzzles, and one which science cannot explain with any degree of certainty.

Whilst referring to anemones one might mention an extraordinary fact which is known about them owing to the act of a naturalist nearly a century and a half ago. The bare information is often given in books, but evidently from third or fourth hand sources, and incorrectly at that. The writer, however, knew very well the famous British marine biologist (the late Professor D'Arcy Thompson) who has related the truth—and this extract from his delightful tale would satisfy even the news editor of a Sunday paper.

The story concerns the possible age which may be reached by an anemone, and the first surprising thing is that we know anything at all about it, seeing that age is a feature of wild things concerning which little is generally known. The

116

The wealth of life on the underside of a dead coral boulder. Green algae (*Caulerpa* and *Halimeda*) compound ascidians, sponges, hydroids, limy tube-worms and encrusting colonies of Bryozoa all compete for space and food. *Photo. Isobel Bennett.*

staggering fact is the actual age reached by the one anemone which by chance became a sort of pet. Here then is the true story as revealed by D'Arcy Thompson.

'The anemone was collected by a Scottish Laird, Sir John Graham Dalyell, about the year 1827. And neither he nor anybody else could tell how old it was then. He took it home, put it in a little bowl on a table by the window, and fed it once a week or so with bits of oyster or mussell; and he changed the sea water every day. And it lived and flourished, and brought forth children and grandchildren; and the years passed away and still the anemone lived on—and it was Sir John who died. And he left it to Professor Fleming, who also was a fine old naturalist, and knew about many things, especially about shells; and in the natural course of things the old professor died. And then the anemone came into the hands of Dr. MacBain, an old Scottish surgeon who, in his young days, had seen many adventures and had made several voyages to Greenland and Davis Straits in the old Dundee and Peterhead whalers. And the sea-anemone, which by now had come to be known as "Granny" and was greatly respected, continued to prosper, and in my boyhood I knew her and the old surgeon well and intimately, and helped to feed her and got some of her children and grandchildren to keep.

'And Dr. MacBain died, and Granny was taken care of for a while by an old lady who kept a girls' school—until she—that is, the old lady—died. And then Granny got into the keeping of a certain botanist; and I don't know exactly what happened, but things went wrong. It cannot well have been that he forgot to feed her, for I have heard of sea-anemones living for months, even for a couple of years, without any food at all. Probably he forgot to change her sea water, which is a much more serious thing for a sea-anemone. At any rate poor Granny died, though almost up to the very last she had been in the best of health. And this was in the year 1887, just sixty years after she had left the pool in the rocks at North Berwick.

'And she was given an obituary notice half a column long in the *Scotsman* newspaper; and very few people, only the great and famous, get as much as that.'

So, a common anemone of the seashore, a small thing consisting chiefly of water (but water bound up in living tissues, which makes all the difference), may live over sixty years!

5

Shells, Sea-stars and other Creatures

Visitors who go 'fossicking' about the exposed coral reefs at low tide or who look through the glass-bottomed boats at submerged coral reefs see many strange creatures about which they ask dozens of questions. Now a man who makes a hobby of 'fossicking' or, say, shell collecting, can find lots of interesting specimens on the shores of South Australia or New South Wales, for example. But there is something quite different about a coral reef. Its beauties and its peculiarities advertise themselves for everyone. It's fun to go exploring!

Naturally coral reefs in different seas have different animal 'companions', but a few are characteristic of coral everywhere, and even if they are not the same species they are close relations, and perhaps to the ordinary person even look to be the same. Similarly we have kangaroos in all the States of Australia, but the keen observer can see that there are many different kinds.

There are thousands of animal and plant species which find the conditions of the Barrier Reef area fully satisfying, and many books would be necessary to describe even half of them. There are other animals which are so much more limited in their needs or restricted in some way that they are found only in the northern parts or the southern parts respectively. This section includes pictures of a few kinds which are so striking on most Barrier Reef shores that they cannot be missed.

Let us first take just a few of the shells, of which there are a great many kinds. One simply can't think of the Barrier Reef without calling to mind the huge clam, the biggest bivalve shell in the world, now and of all time. There are at least four kinds (three species of one genus, *Tridacna*, and the famous horseshoe clam, *Hippopus*) and, as usual, amazing stories are told of the big sizes reached. The writer happens to have seen the heaviest known pair of shells, which are used as fonts for holy water in the Cathedral of St. Sulpice, Paris. One often finds the dead clam shells lying on their sides, but in life the animal occupies quite a different position and one sees it either on the sandy shores or half embedded in the coral itself, sitting with its hinge downwards and the opening upwards so that one looks straight down into it. The giant species (*Tridacna gigas*) is usually found exposed on the reef-flats in northern Barrier Reef waters. The species which peep upwards from holes in the coral have actually bored these holes in the coral in which they live.

As extraordinary as their size is the brilliant colour of the flesh (mantle) which lines the shell and is exposed when they gape open. This colour varies from brown and olive to a brilliant blue. No matter how big the animal may be, this shellfish feeds only on the microscopic life in the sea water, which it sucks in when the tide covers it. But that coloured and thick edge of the mantle is extraordinary for another reason. The colour is largely due to the presence of myriads of little plants (single-celled plants known as zooxanthellae) living inside the flesh of the animal.

There is no doubt that this curious position of very tiny plants living in the flesh of an animal is a partnership, and that here as in the corals it is of advantage to the plant cells which get protection as well as some of their food requirements from the waste substances of the clam. The latter, however, unlike the corals, is not carnivorous, and there is a theory of deliberate 'farming' of the single-celled plants by the clams for food. But there is considerable argument about it still.

The clam should be exciting enough for the fossicker without anything further, since, without question, it is one of the most peculiar bivalves in the world in its life habits; but attached to it is one of the most impressive yarns of the Barrier Reef. The story is that native fishermen hunting after bêche-de-mer, and other things, have, on occasion, trodden by accident on a big open clam in such a way that one foot has slipped inside the shells, which have closed on it quickly so as to imprison the unfortunate victim. Divers without breathing apparatus are supposed to have been caught below water and drowned, and even lonely shore fishermen are supposed to have been held until drowned. No one has yet doubted the possibility of this happening (possibly rarely and only with big clams), but no authentic cases seem to have been recorded. Experiments with dummy limbs have been tried, but these were cases where the limb was deliberately inserted. In life the valves of the clam are usually not more than an inch or so apart and they tend to close rather than open when approached.

THE BAILER SHELL

Almost as though not content with the world's largest bivalve, the Barrier Reef presents also to our view two very big univalve shells (although they are not to be compared with the big clams for size). One is the so-called bailer shell (*Melo amphoras*), which with luck may be seen creeping over the coral sand at low tide as in the photograph on page 126. More usually in daylight hours it lies almost buried in the sand. This animal feeds in a different manner altogether from the stationary clam, and goes about seeking for its food, which consists of small shellfish. In front, waving almost like an elephant's trunk, is a tube (siphon) through which sea water is sucked. The shell is a cream brown in colour and the big foot is a grey or brown, flecked with small light-coloured spots. The name 'bailer' has been given because the natives really use the empty shell for bailing water, and indeed as a kind of domestic pot for all sorts of purposes.

THE SPIDER SHELL

Another very large 'snail' which is familiar to all visitors to the coral reefs of the Great Barrier area is the so-called spider shell (*Lambis lambis*). It is a familiar object, too, on coral islands far distant from Australia.

One edge of the shell mouth is prolonged into long curved spines and the interior of this shell mouth is of a beautiful pink, burnt orange or red colour. This is one of the most active of molluscs and it will generally perform if (when crawling) it is turned over on its back.

CONE SHELLS

There are several different kinds of cone shells, some of which counted amongst the most desired and valuable shells in the days when shell-collecting was a great hobby. Shells with the animal alive are worthy of special attention today because an old story of the native fishermen of Torres Strait that these creatures can kill a man (a story regarded with some doubt in the past) has been proved true. An Australian, a visitor to the Great Barrier Reef, was the victim, and this has led to a considerable amount of research being carried out both on the mechanism of the 'bites' and antidotes to its poison.

The animal of the cone shell is unique among gastopods in that it can give a quick and poisonous stab when disturbed. The potency of this stab must put it in the ranks of the most poisonous of all animals.† (The larger specimens must only be picked up with very great care, and preferably they should be scooped up with something and not taken into the hand.) Of all the thousands of kinds of molluscs in all the world's seas, only the cone shells can do this. So be careful!

PEARL AND OTHER 'OYSTERS'

The visitor to the northern end of the Great Barrier Reef area—to Thursday Island, for example—will be attracted by the different kinds of pearlshell, and the pearlshell industry. There is another kind of pearlshell of quite small size and valuable only for its pearls, which is found especially in Shark's Bay on the coast of Western Australia.

Incidentally, although usually called pearl 'oysters', they do not belong to the same family as true oysters at all, but what's in a name? This might seem to be an appalling question to come from a zoologist, but the zoologists can use their scientific names and so far they have not agreed amongst themselves about classifying the bivalves. All my readers need is the fact that pearlshells are bivalves, and if they are going into the industry they can use the striking names 'gold-lip' and 'black-lip'. Over 1,400 tons weight of these 'mother of pearl' shells were taken from northern Australian waters during the 1960–1 season. These shells have to be obtained by divers and usually only small shells (never more than 3–4 in.) are found on intertidal reefs along the Queensland coast.

Excellent edible rock oysters are common on many coral reefs, and usually one has the satisfaction of knowing that these are most certainly uncontaminated by sewage, a fact

---

†Research by Dr. R. Endean of the University of Queensland seems to indicate that not all cones are dangerous to man. The poison of those cones which feed on fish is toxic to vertebrates, but those which feed on worms, other molluscs, etc., seem to be harmless.

which cannot always be accepted as true for those from the closer settlements of human populations.

Bell-tent-shaped trochus shells, once so important in the button industry, used to be common on the exposed reefs at low tide, but the industrious Japanese fishermen in pre-war days 'did' for these, and the trochus like the pearl oyster has had to be collected by divers. However, the invention of plastics has been a severe blow to trochus-shell fishermen.

COWRIES

We should not leave this brief reference to the shells without mentioning the ever popular cowries with their beautiful glossy outside surface, which looks as if it had been specially polished. There are several species, ranging in colour from the perfect glossy cream and relatively small 'money cowrie', used by the Pacific islanders for decoration as well as cash, to larger species like the 'tiger' cowrie. Some pattern in which a rich brown prevails on a light background is frequent. The beautiful glossy surface of the shell is due to the fact that the fleshy mantle of the cowrie animal, which secretes the shell, can be expanded to cover the whole surface. This mantle may be seen when the animals are crawling about. In practically all other molluscs the mantle remains inside the shell which it made. So the outside of the shell gets scratched and rubbed with no chance of any repair.

SEA-STARS AND THEIR ALLIES

We shall now take a group of animals which are all closely related, although the non-scientist would scarcely believe it. It comprises starfish (or sea-stars as some prefer to call them), the sausage-shaped bêche-de-mer, and the almost spherical spiny sea-urchins.

You will be pardoned for saying that you see no resemblance whatever between these three sorts of creatures. All

Great Barrier Reef Clam *(Tridacna)* which bores in dead coral. (Top)
Giant clam shells *(Tridacna* sp.). —*Photo. Isobel Bennett.*

Needle-spined Sea Urchin *(Diadema setosa)* in pools at low water, Great Barrier Reef.

Bailer Shell of the Great Barrier Reefs.

Cowrie, with mantle partly extended.
—*Photo. Gwen Burns.*

Cone shells from the Great Barrier Reefs. Molluscs of this group have a very poisonous bite *(Conus marmoreus* and *C. textile* respectively.)

Bêche-de-mer amongst coral in pools on flat at low water, Hayman Island.

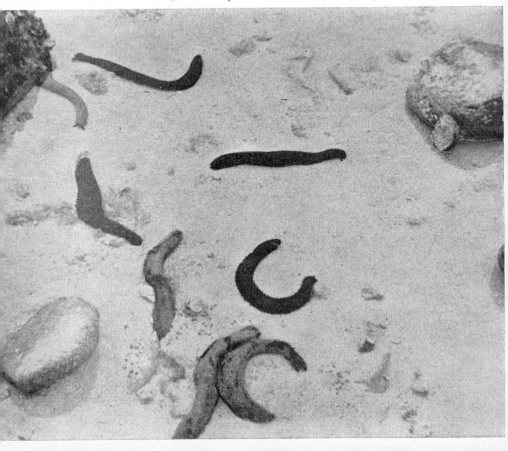

Native spearing fish, Whitsunday Island waters.

One of the Squillas or prawn-killers, a close relation of *Gonodactylus,* showing the raptorial claw, and (right) the Pistol Prawn and its snapping nipper. —*Photos. Gwen Burns.*

The Walking Fish *(Periophthalmus),* common amidst muddy shallows of coral islands in the northern part of the Great Barrier Reef area. —*Photo. Donald F. Thomson.*

Butterfly Cod, of the coral pools, Great Barrier Reef and Lord Howe Island.

Soldier Crabs *(Mictyris longicarpus)* on a sand flat.

The Ghost Crab *(Ocypode ceratophthalma),* very common high up on the sandy beaches of Barrier Reef islands. —*Photo. Gwen Burns.*

the same, the resemblance is there if you look very carefully.

The most unusual starfish, and one which is quite unlike any found on the shores of New South Wales or the southern shores of Australia, is a large five-armed species with a hard upper surface which is covered with coloured nodules. Specimens are sometimes found on the bottom of the Barrier Reef Channel, but frequently they can be picked up in large numbers on the shores of one of the Whitsunday Islands. The fact is that they migrate with the seasons; they winter in the deeper water and spend the summer close to or on the shores at low tide. The photograph shows an occasion when dozens of them were found by a tourist party at low tide on the sandy shore of a bay on Hook Island. This animal bears the scientific name *Protoreaster nodosus* and has no common name. You cannot forget this beautiful starfish, which belongs to a family inhabiting the tropical seas of the East Indies and north-eastern Australia.

Another striking starfish is the blue *Linckia*. This also is large, sometimes reaching about ten inches across, but it is the bright blue colour which is the astonishing feature, for such a blue is very unusual on starfish. Like others of its relatives it crawls about on hundreds of little hollow feet (tube feet) which project on the underside of the arms. These little feet are actually extended by sea water so that the locomotive mechanism is hydraulic plus muscles.

THE SEA-URCHINS

The most striking sea-urchin of the coral pools is one with long, needle-like spines, *Diadema setosa*. Sea-urchins are very common along most of the Australian coast, and one can find thousands of quite long-spined sea-urchins in Sydney Harbour. They are purple-black in colour and very close relations of the needle-spined urchins of the coral reefs. But none of these sea-urchins has such long, delicate

133

and sharp spines as those of the coral pools of the Great Barrier Reef area and shores of north and north-western Australia, and this makes the latter very unpleasant to tackle, although they look most beautiful. They seem almost to live in families, so many occur together. Their spines are needle sharp, and very brittle, so that it is quite easy, if one is not careful, to get a piece of one broken off into one's skin. The consequence may be a serious wound, so—you have been warned!

On some of the coral flats there are hundreds of a short-spined sea-urchin, *Echinometra mathei*, each of which is snugly lying in a hole which it has made for itself in the half rotten coral. Probably this particular kind of urchin ranks amongst the most numerous of all the animals which inhabit the world's coral shores. It is plentiful on the reefs of West Australia's Abrolhos Islands, at Lord Howe and very numerous on some of the Barrier Reef Islands.

BÊCHE-DE-MER (TREPANG)

The bêche-de-mer is a queer, ugly-looking, sausage-shaped animal mostly dark in colour, red and brown to black. Usually one sees them lying in a pool with a sandy or gravelly bottom. Look at the mouth surrounded by feathery tentacles at one end. Like some big worms they continually swallow mud, gravel or sand and live on the organic matter which they can extract from it as it goes through their intestines. Probably they shift tons in this way in a year. Such is their activity that they must be counted amongst the most important creatures which pulverize still further the rotting coral rock. Their most extraordinary character is the peculiar habit of throwing out all their insides when molested. They simply grow another set of internal organs.

One would scarcely have imagined that anyone would have found such animals desirable as food, but the Chinese discovered a taste for them long ago, and a taste so keen as to encourage fishing in far distant seas. This is said to be the oldest fishery of the Barrier Reef. Probably some retired 'white men' from the East also learned to appreciate the flavour or consistency, because the writer used to see trepang for sale in Piccadilly, London. But that was long, long ago too!

The bêche-de-mer is used to make soup. The skin only is kept, and this is cured by smoking, and dried until it is hard as wood.

The scientist calls all these animals Holothurians, and the European species have been popularly called sea-cucumbers, but none of them seem edible, or at least are not utilized for edible purposes. They are all very slow-moving animals and quite harmless, of a brown, or striped brown colour.

A long and snake-like inedible but delicate species (*Synapta maculata*) which is not uncommon in coral pools of the northern reefs has quite a thin and apparently very 'sticky' skin. It may reach a length of more than three or four feet. A piece of this skin under a microscope would reveal a myriad of tiny limy spicules beautifully shaped, which by virtue of their number, give a certain stability to the animals.

CRABS, PRAWNS, AND OTHER CRUSTACEA

So far we have spoken of the slow-moving animals of the coral reefs (or of animals which, like the oyster, remain fixed in their adult stage). The coral pools are, however, enlivened by lively creatures too, amongst which we must count the fish and the crustacea.

Crabs are perhaps the comedians of our seashores and coral pools, and they are certainly plentiful. Some arouse curiosity by their beautiful colouring, others by their quaint habits. They are commonly seen wandering over the reef-flats, hiding under dead coral boulders, or living among the

135

branches of the corals. One very ingenious small crab (the so-called gall-forming crab) actually causes the corals to form a protective cover for it.

Although many kinds of crabs are, like fish, adapted for living and breathing under water, there are some which have almost become land animals, and strangely enough they make up in numbers for their lack of variety of species. Take the ghost crabs, for example (*Ocypode*). The make burrows in the dry sand above high-water mark and usually only come out at night. I shall never forget waking up one night when -leeping on a camp bed in a small tent on a coral island shore. There was an extraordinary rustling and scraping going on about me. I grabbed a torch and saw with amazement that the sand was literally covered with dazed ghost crabs, which usually move like lightning when disturbed. There was no space between them—they seemed countless. They are not called ghost crabs because of their nightly prowls, but because their colouring matches the sand so well that if they do leave their burrows by day, they are almost invisible to the eye. This crab (two species) is just as common on the coral islands of the Great Barrier, and they are serious enemies of the little newly-hatched turtles (see pages 57 and 131).

Amongst other crabs more or less of the land are the soldier crabs and the fiddler crabs. The soldier crabs are, as the French would say, a 'type' of their own, and strangely enough they are to be found along the entire coast of eastern Australia wherever there are sand beaches with a little mud. They appear suddenly, and as if from nowhere, when the receding tide is about two hours from low water. They have pushed themselves up from below the wet sand, and, being hungry, they proceed to feed on the scum covering the sand. But for some reason (probably not even known to themselves) they like company, and as they go feeding, they crowd more and more together. The name 'soldier' is really quite incorrect because they separate and scuttle away in all directions if one tries to approach with a camera. Their 'armies' are mere 'mobs'. There are several other curious things about them, one being that they walk in a 'mincing' manner, but forwards, whilst all other crabs walk sideways. With their vivid blue colouring they are unmistakable.

The fiddler crabs make holes in the mud. The name has been given because the male has one claw which is brightly coloured pink to red, and about as big as the rest of the body. This animal has the habit of sitting at the top of its burrow and waving its huge appendage as an enticement to some female. The invitation may have appeared to someone to look like fiddling, but it also looks as if a small man were trying to attract attention by waving a 'cello, with a kind of 'come hither' movement. These crabs are found on sandy-muddy shore throughout the world's tropics.

Little prawns dart hither and thither in the pools and among the corals. There are many other interesting crustacea. One type that is certain to arouse interest if it comes the visitor's way is the striking 'prawn killer" as it is called. Species are fairly common on most coral reefs of the world, and they are often seen when dead coral boulders are over-turned, but it is not so easy to catch them for they move like lightning. The illustration (see page 129) should be quite sufficient to reveal the creature's interest. It looks deadly with its strange claws which close up like the blades of a clasp knife. But no clasp knife is made with rows of sharp spines on the edge of its blades, and the lightning-like rapidity of the prawn killer in all its movements makes it a good example of murderous beauty. Large species of *Pseudo-squilla* and *Lysiosquilla* are common in Australian tropical waters, but the commonest form bound on intertidal reefs is the smaller but beautifully marked *Gonodactylus*, which though not so well armed on the clasp-knife-like claw nevertheless gets its prey.

THE PISTOL PRAWN

If, on a quiet beach, you hear curious cracks about you, like someone breaking pieces of glass, you will know that pistol prawns are about. During the last few decades they have become well known to many men who formerly had little or no interest in the animals of the sea! I refer to sailors of the British and American navies. With the intention of capturing enemy submarines, science was called on to invent new methods for their detection. Amongst these was an instrument which magnified the sounds made below the surface of the sea. To the surprise of the navy men, one could hear not only propellers and waves, but all sorts of quaint sounds made by fish and other creatures, and the loudest and most surprising of these were the 'snaps' of the pistol prawn. Of course the identity of some of the sounds was not discovered without some trouble, and the zoologist and the submarine hunter were brought together to seek an explanation of the noises. This was fortunate, because the marine zoologist, who knew the sound of the pistol prawn very well, had never been 'stimulated' into finding out how the extraordinary sharp cracking sound was made. Now we know. The animal snaps closed its big claws, but there is a special mechanism which acts like a trigger and releases the moving claw very suddenly so that it hits the other one with great force. (See page 129.) Today, with the advent of the vision and the tape recorder, the causes of more and more underwater noises are being discovered.

THE FISHES

Because there are so many fish in Great Barrier Reef waters, we cannot possibly attempt to do justice to them, and so this reference will certainly fail to satisfy the keen fisherman. After all, he would need local advice in any case, and we suggest he seeks it and follows it.

Roughly speaking, the visitors to coral reefs will be attracted by two kinds of fish: the little brightly coloured fish of the coral reef pools, which do not come into the angler's programme; and the larger edible, and possibly inedible, fish which provide fun for the fisherman as well as food for the table. We include in this second group not only fish attractive in appearance and in flavour, but also sharks and rays. Possibly we should make a third class to include only one kind of fish, and a small fellow at that, which can spend a considerable part of its time on land, and out of water altogether. This is of course a very unscientific classification, but the little fish that we have separated from the rest has habits which are most unusual. It loves the mud of mangrove swamps and the pools of coral islands, especially in the tropics, and because it hops about out of water altogether it is called the mud skipper or the walking fish (*Periophthalmus argentilmeatus*). Its large spherical eyes on the top of its head must be specially adapted for seeing in the air, because it is quick to take off if one tries to catch it. And of course its gills must also be specially suited for air breathing. With this reference we can leave this most curious but not exactly beautiful fish species and turn to those permanent inhabitants of the sea.

The tiny coral fish swim in shoals about the picturesque submerged corals. They are gloriously coloured. In fact the existence of shoals of coloured fish is a feature of all coral reefs. Their colours are the most brilliant blues and greens, with a range from orange to purple to complete the entire spectrum. There is no doubt whatever about the association of the most gorgeously coloured fish with coral, but considerable doubt exists as to *why* this should be so. Most writers take it for granted that there is some attempt at camouflage here. Perhaps we, ourselves, had better keep 'in shallow water' and leave it at that!

One or two species of these fish deliberately choose to live

139

amidst the tentacles of the big carnivorous anemones, but as already noted this association appears advantageous to both. But how on earth is it that the fish is immune, or, more than that, is left undisturbed by the batteries of stinging cells and the tentacles of the anemone? The slightest touch of any other animal seems to bring the anemone into action with its tentacles contracting on the intruder. Can it be that the lowly anemone recognizes some quality in its fish partner and leaves it unmolested because of what it gains in turn? One fish that lives within the anemone is a bright vermilion in colour with white cross bands.

Slowly and stately amidst the coral floats the most beautifully marked of all coral fishes—the butterfly cod (*Pterois volitans*). Its great wing-like pectoral fins and its narrow cross bands of dark and light colours make it a creature of great beauty. It used to be quite common amidst the coral growths of Lord Howe Island as well as in the Great Barrier Reef area. But such creatures need government protection, even though their beauty is most transient, and disappears with the death of the little fish, which only specialists with the equipment of great aquaria could hope to keep alive. (We might add that it should be handled with care. Its spines are venomous.)

We cannot possibly complete this reference to the fishes of the Great Barrier Reef pools (fishes which are looked at rather than angled) without an account of the stone fish (*Synanceja trachynis*), which is very ugly, and unfortunately not easily seen. Dr. Yonge puts it down as the most hideous of all living creatures. It frequents those beautiful pools of the reefs, camouflaged by its colour and general appearance. Actually one must admire its ugly coloration and form because of its strikingly efficient resemblance to its background. The stone fish is mentioned here because a warning of its dreaded poisonous spines is absolutely essential. Probably it was one of the first dangers of the coral shores to be made known to

Banfield of Dunk Island by the aborigines. He described in detail (*Confessions of a Beachcomber*) how they dread it, christening it with such titles as sea-devil, the warty ghoul, and the sea-scorpion.

It is difficult to say how numerous these fish are, because probably most are not seen. Warnings enough have been issued to make visitors and fishermen wear boots when fossicking amidst the coral growths at low tide. It is these boulders which the fish resembles to the highest degree. I have never seen one in its pool. Dr. Yonge, after a year, said he had never distinguished one either, but the keen-eyed aborigines picked them out. Normally the fish just waits until a crab or small fish (which apparently is equally blind to its presence) comes within range of its mouth. Then it suddenly opens this trap and its prey disappears. Unfortunately this is not all. The danger to human beings is that it is so easy to tread on one with a bare foot. Then tragedy begins! The fish has a row of strong and needle-sharp spines along the middle of the back and to each of these poison glands are connected. Any contact with the fish causes it instantly to raise the spines vertically, almost as if they possessed springs, instead of muscles. According to local belief days of agony follow an untreated sting, if the person poisoned manages to escape death. Today, however, medical research has provided effective measures for treating stonefish wounds.

Now let us turn to what the angler calls fish. There are tasty fish, large fish, and good-looking fish in the waters of these coral seas. At times the lucky fisherman who is trolling meets a shoal of big pelagic fish—perhaps the most likely being Spanish mackerel. This is a well-known attraction to the Barrier Reef waters and seems to provide all that the angler desires. Its season is between May and October, varying somewhat according to locality. Other related pelagic fish which come into the category of game fish are tuna (different species, bonito, etc.). There are also queenfish and kingfish and occasional marlin. The more ordinary angler may excite himself with the prospect of catching large red emperors, coral trout, coral cod, king snapper, sweetlip and blue-spotted groper. All coral reefs seem to abound with brilliantly coloured species of parrot fish, and often at low tide large shoals of them may be disturbed when one is walking across shallow sandy pools or the reef-flats.

Sharks are unfortunately only too numerous in the coral seas, many species like the tiger shark and the grey nurse being of wide range, and known on distant shores. If, however, a black-list of human victims is set down, the number for the Barrier Reef area is small compared with that for Australia's more southern waters, but this is probably only a consequence of the difference in the number of bathers in the two regions. After all, the more pedestrians the greater the number of street accidents. Probably the true list of shark tragedies for the coral reefs of the north of Australia where the pearl divers work will never be known. A tendency to keep the number small is accentuated because of the firmly established belief in many parts of the world that sharks are not so dangerous after all. The big groper is certainly to be painted in colours as bad, because of its reputation for attacking divers or their gear. But we of New South Wales have no doubts about the truth of shark stories. We have been too close to deaths caused by them, and seen the horrible results too often to disbelieve. No doubt, for some reason as yet unexplained, sharks may be less likely to attack human beings in some other tropic or sub-tropical waters. I have seen fearless swimmers near the coral reefs of Ceylon, Nauru and other places. There was no enclosed swimming bath at Nauru. The marine scientists who know the coral reef waters of Bermuda and Florida regard their sharks as practically harmless.

Those close relatives of the sharks, the rays, are also common in the warm waters of the north. Some of the rays are of striking size, and not infrequently specimens of the devil fish are taken. This species of ray has two extraordinary horn-like flippers projecting in front of the head. It grows to a width of at least thirteen feet in Australian waters, but the species is not confined to the coral region, and a picture in the *Illustrated Sydney News* of March 1868 shows one being pulled ashore in Sydney Harbour.

Despite the giant size of the devil fish, it feeds on very small organisms and so has no fearsome mouth to trouble the swimmer. Nor has it poisonous spines like the stingrays, which are therefore far more dangerous to bathers, divers and fishermen; in fact the devil ray is quite harmless.

6

The Puzzle of the Origin of Barrier Reefs and Atolls

THE red coral of the Bible and of jewellers was still a puzzle to the philosophers in the days of the ancient Greeks, at the time when Aristotle had already recognized that anemones were animals. After all, fishermen-divers who collected it could not help seeing that this red coral from the Mediterranean Sea actually grew with branches something like a plant. As for the individual polyps, no other sea animals in life look so much like little flowers. Notwithstanding this, it is not really surprising that two thousand years ago most corals were generally regarded as of mineral origin.

It may be noted here that the 'red coral' which has been so much used in jewellery, and which was valued even three or four thousand years ago, is not a true coral of the group which plays so big a part in building up reefs. It is closely related, however, to the *soft* corals, which, as we have noted, are very common on the shores of Barrier Reef islands.

Thus centuries had to pass away before the coral reefs familiar to the ancients in the Red Sea area came definitely to be recognized as something living, and even then the reef-forming coral was wrongly classed as a plant. In the long years after 'red coral' itself came to be suspected of being a live thing, the more delicate branching corals remained a mystery, and with much argument they were placed in each of the kingdoms, mineral, plant, and animal, until André de Peysonnel, a citizen of Marseilles, kept living coral in aquaria, studied it closely, and, in 1727, expounded his views—that these growths were animal in nature—before the French Academy of Sciences. Like many other pioneers of this world, he was rather badly treated, and twenty-four more years passed by before the Royal Society of London accepted his views as the truth.

Peysonnel spent thirty years studying reef corals, and prepared the scientific world for the idea that not only were the delicate branching corals animal in their nature, but that the massive coral products of the sea were of the same class.

Yet all this argument about the nature of coral did nothing to reveal that there was a really great puzzle in the existence of coral islands. The fascinating atolls of the Pacific were, however, scarcely known to Europeans in the year 1800 and the nature of barrier reefs had not dawned on the scientists of the day.

As one might easily guess, the first coral reefs to stir up scientific curiosity were the ring-like atolls of the Indian and Pacific oceans. Indeed, they interested everyone. They could not but arouse the highest degree of puzzlement amongst the early navigators as well as amongst the whalers, simple sailors, and the advance guard of marine commercials. What tales they brought home about those distant places and their inhabitants! And what courage those ancient mariners displayed, knowing and fearing as they must have done the power of treacherous reefs to wreck their frail ships, yet always sailing on through unchartered seas.

It would be impossible to do justice here to all the theories and beliefs that have been put forward since 1830 to explain the origin of atolls and barrier reefs. It would make a tale equal to any detective story and one of greater variety. There is no more fascinating chapter in the history of marine science than this, nor one which breathes more of adventure and uncertainty. The 'detectives' are still at it today, and they are now using the latest weapons of science. Uncertainty still remains, especially in regard to any particular reefs or islands, for the wise man will not conclude hastily that all have originated through a similar sequence of events.

It may come as a surprise to the ordinary man, or even to the politician, that some scientists in the United States today are tackling the coral reef problem on a bigger scale than ever, despite the fact that the investigations have nothing to do with profit-making, commerce, or war. (War has only helped to release some funds.) Thank heaven there are still scientists who choose to study nature because they are curious, and find happiness in adventures of this kind. Make no mistake about this, although you will probably be as surprised as was the present writer to find that our story ends with the atomic bomb.

An American specialist on coral reefs, the late W. M. Davis, wrote that 'the atolls are inscrutable structures'. They have certainly been at the centre of the coral-reef problem, so let us turn to them first, even though they are not well developed in Australian seas.

One of the first names in the modern story of coral islands is that of a remarkable German named Chamisso, who was not only a naturalist but a poet and writer. It is a very strange thing that hundreds of thousands of young English-speaking students who are learning German have been made to translate and use as a text a little story he wrote called *Peter Schlemihl, or the Man who Lost his Shadow*. Very few of these young people realize that Chamisso played a part in early oceanic exploration, travelling across the Pacific and writing remarkably good descriptions of coral reefs. It was in 1815–18 that Chamisso took part in a voyage to the South Pacific coral seas under the leadership of one Kotzebue. He was especially fascinated by the atolls and after seeing some

146

of them he propounded the simple theory that a mass of coral grew up until it reached the ocean surface and then the corals thrived better on the outside, where they were well washed by the surf. The consequence of this would be that the coral foundation tended to form a ring and an ever-widening ring, too, in the middle of which would be a lagoon where the coral succumbed owing to lack of food, and was subjected to erosion and destruction by all sorts of agents. Chamisso probably thought of the fairy rings which one sometimes sees on grassy meadows, and which are due to the outward growth of fungi. He saw some resemblance to the growth of a ring of coral in this phenomenon of the fields.

It was the ring shape of the atolls which interested him, as indeed it has excited so many others. Chamisso's effort at explanation was clever and it certainly heightened the romantic conception aroused by these little islands of the Pacific. The shape of atolls and the presence of a calm lagoon inside a reef of living rock continued for years to puzzle everyone. In fact we still haven't done with the lagoon whether it be circular or a long channel like that of the Great Barrier Reef. The scientific problems concerning the lagoon are in fact bewildering in many ways.

The great puzzle of the atolls and barrier reefs is, however, the matter of their foundations. Chamisso couldn't guess that he was missing this puzzle because at that time the conditions of life which reef-building corals require were practically unknown to science and no one realized that such coral would only grow in shallow water. In any case, charting of the ocean depths had scarcely commenced.

A great change in the situation was soon to come. In fact, Kotzebue's expedition with Chamisso took some trouble to measure the depths in the lagoon of an atoll, and surprise was expressed that the outer edge of the reefs sloped so steeply to depths that were beyond measurement. But the

Diagrams showing origin of coral atolls according to Darwin.

Stage 1—Island with surrounding fringing coral reef (coral shown black)

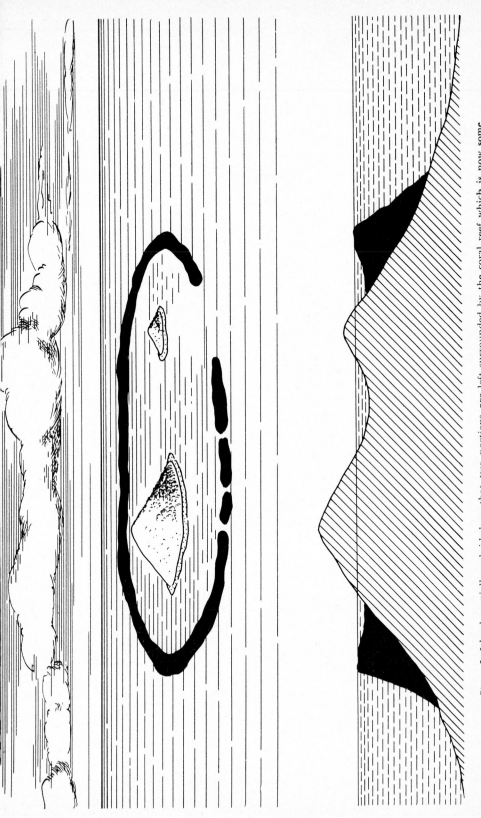

Stage 2—Island partially subsided so that two portions are left surrounded by the coral reef which is now some little distance from the island shores. The reef is now called a *Barrier* Reef (see definition in text).

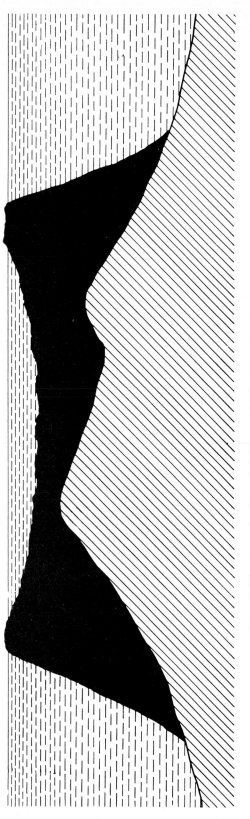

Stage 3—Island completely sunk below sea level. The ring-shaped reef is an *Atoll*.

"Traffic lines" among the corals. —*Photo. Australian Museum.*

A unique photograph of *Fungia*, the mushroom coral, with the polyp partly extended. —*Photo. Allen Keast.*

Massive type of reef building coral *(Goniopora)* on fringing reef of Seaforth Island.

An atoll of the coral seas, as illustrated in early works on the coral islands of the Pacific Ocean.

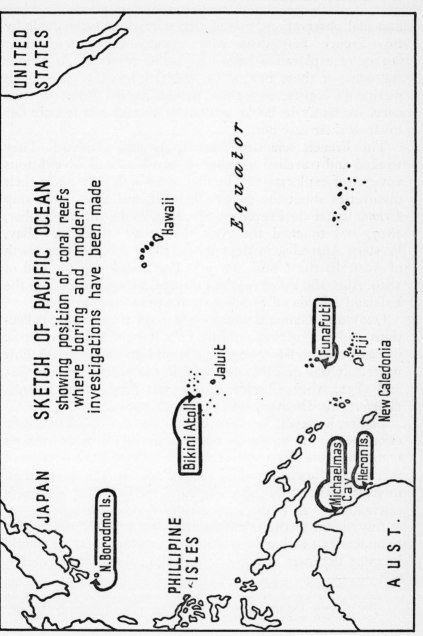

SKETCH OF PACIFIC OCEAN

showing position of coral reefs
where boring and modern
investigations have been made

UNITED STATES

JAPAN

Hawaii

Equator

Jaluit

Bikini Atoll

Funafuti

Fiji

New Caledonia

N.Borodmo Is.

PHILLIPINE ISLES

Michaelmas Cay

Heron Is.

A U S T.

Sketch map of Pacific Ocean showing position of coral reefs where boring and modern
investigations have been made.

first real observations that altered everything were made by two French naturalists who actually commenced their voyage of exploration before Kotzebue returned. And since the work of these men is of special interest to Australian marine biologists, and their names receive little prominence—certainly in books written in English—it is only fair to stress their case here.

The French scientists were Quoy and Gaimard. They worked and travelled together on two long and adventurous voyages of exploration. The first, on which they made their discoveries about the growth of coral, was that of the ship *Uranie* under de Freycinet. She left Toulon in September, 1817, and touched the Australian coast at Shark's Bay, Western Australia, in September, 1818. After sailing north of Australia the *Uranie* put into Port Jackson at the end of 1819. Alas, she never reached Europe, being wrecked on the Falkland Islands off South America the following year.

Quoy and Gaimard saved their lives if not their collections, and in 1825 they published the statement (in a scientific journal) that reef-forming coral would grow only in shallow water.* It was quickly confirmed in the years between 1825 and 1831, when Charles Darwin left England in H.M.S. *Beagle*. This discovery had amazing consequences.

Before, however, we turn to this the first great scientific effort in the life of young Darwin, we might proclaim with truth that this discovery of the limitation in the growth of reef corals (not *all* corals) to shallow water should be of interest, and should make the coral reefs of Australian seas fascinating, even to the least curious holiday-maker.

Any visitor to the Great Barrier Reef area should be able to understand without any trouble whatever that there should be great expanses of fringing reef close along the seashores,

---

*Quoy and Gaimard's second voyage shows that they had not been frightened by the rigours and shipwreck of their first. It was the famous voyage (1826-9) of the *Astrolabe* under Dumont d'Urville. The *Astrolabe* sailed round the world, visited Australian seas, and a fine account of the scientific work accomplished resulted.

in the shallow water of both islands and mainland; but we should expect his query: 'How did the coral reefs of the Outer Barrier grow up from the bottom of the sea if it has always been as deep as it is at present?' We should expect him to say, 'Is there a bar, a shoal, or some sort of submarine platform nearly parallel to the coast on which the reefs of the Outer Barrier have grown—or how?'

We shall try and tell in the simplest possible way something of the story of this puzzle and of man's attempts to solve it during the last hundred years. Incidentally, we shall have quite a lot to say about the masterly theory propounded by Charles Darwin (who is practically known to the world only as the originator of a theory of evolution). Darwin was a young man of twenty-seven when he commenced his famous voyage round the world in H.M.S. *Beagle* in 1831. He evidently knew something of the fascinating atolls before he started, and he must have had some idea of the difficulties in explaining them.

Already, however, several other scientists had tried to explain the ring-like shape of atolls and the fact that they were surrounded by deep ocean waters, by suggesting that they were simply indicative of the presence of extinct volcanoes under the sea. They could then account for the ring-like coral growth by assuming it was a relatively thin coral covering over the rim of a crater which was not far below the sea's surface when the coral commenced to grow. The central lagoon would of course represent the flooded crater itself. This was quite a natural deduction to make and the theory was for a time very popular. Incidentally, Quoy and Gaimard were about the first to suggest this explanation in 1825. Many visitors to coral islands today can picture a resemblance between coral atolls and the summits of submerged volcanoes. The theory explains the lagoon as well as the reef. But no volcanoes are known on land with craters as wide as the atolls of the Indian Ocean. And in any case

155

this still leaves one facing the difficulty of explaining the two giant barrier reefs of the world—that along the coast of Queensland and that along the island of New Caledonia. These are not rings of coral but long lines of reefs, and they also rise from great depths of the sea, too deep for reef coral to flourish.

It was just after Lyell, the famous English geologist, tried to explain the atolls as representing summits of submerged volcanoes that Darwin sailed from England, engaged on his first job, that of a naturalist on one of the surveying ships of the British Navy. In those days it was customary to have a naturalist as a supernumerary on British exploratory vessels. His rank was low but more than once his fame became high. Darwin showed the brilliance of his powers very soon by propounding a scientific theory of coral reefs which in this sphere of marine investigation endures today, after over a hundred years of argument and observation.

Darwin's theory had the merit too that it explained the ringlike atolls as well as barrier reefs; indeed it attracted attention by its simplicity, for it linked up together the growth of all kinds of coral reefs.

Darwin started off with the most simple fact, namely, that wherever the sea is shallow in suitable tropic regions, as for example against the shores of any land, whether it be island or continent, then coral can grow from the sea bottom to the surface and fringing reefs may be formed. There is no problem here at all. The temperature of the sea, the quality of the sea water, and the depth must just be suitable and the young coral animals must be present drifting about in the sea. We have many such fringing reefs as these on the northern coast of Australia, everywhere between the Abrolhos on the west and the southern end of the Great Barrier Reef on the east; and there is the fringing reef on the west side of Lord Howe Island, which like the Abrolhos Isles is surprisingly far south of the equator. There is also a small reef of this kind on the south side of Norfolk Island. There are very many reefs of this nature in the shallow waters of the Great Barrier Reef channel, and as we have seen, many of them growing along the shores of the channel islets (of all kinds) provide the best and most easily reached views of coral.

Usually there is no channel or lagoon between such a fringing reef and the land. The coral is a continuation of the shore itself, and the surface (which is very rough and full of pools) is noteworthy because it is very level. This is the edge of the tropical shore where the tourists go fossicking.

Now, the reader is asked to seize hold of my next point, examining the diagrams as he reads on. Assume that a shallow-water growth of coral like that just described is growing up where the earth's surface happens to be slowly subsiding. (This sort of thing, subsidence and its opposite—uplift—by the way, should be known to every school child; thus Tasmania was once connected to Victoria; England was once joined across to Europe. On the other hand, some parts of the earth which are now mountains were once below the sea.)

If the sea bottom is subsiding where a coral reef is growing upwards, it is easy to understand that this will give the coral a chance to continue growing upwards and so become thicker and thicker during perhaps millions of years. Otherwise growth would have stopped as soon as sea level was reached. The full effect on a growing fringing reef of coral is to make it become much thicker and at the same time (as the diagrams show) the outer margin will gradually become further and further away from the land, whether the land be a small island or the almost straight coast of a continent.

This, then, is the simple way in which Darwin explained the next stage in the formation of an atoll or a barrier reef. The reader will notice that gradually as the bottom subsides the coral near the land fails to reach the sea level, and so a channel or lagoon comes into existence. This will either be ring-shaped if around an island, in the case of atoll formation, or it will be a long channel bounding the coast like that of the Great Barrier Reef area.

The last stage in the formation of an atoll, according to Darwin, is that in which the central island will have sunk completely below the sea, and so there comes to be a lagoon surrounded by a great thickness of coral reef material in the shape of a ring or oval. Finally little islets of sand or broken coral become heaped on this coral base and so stand above sea-level.

If we apply this theory to the coast of Queensland instead of to a little island, we can understand how the rocky continental non-coral islands of the channel were once elevations on the eastern margin of Queensland which have been cut off from the mainland by the sea flooding in as the coastlines subsided. We can also understand the origin of the long series of coral reefs which rise from deep water far from the land and make up the outer barrier of the Great Barrier Reef.

The reader must appreciate that if the theory of Darwin is correct and applies to any particular barrier reef or coral atoll, then one must expect the limy reef material to reach great thicknesses, in fact, to be nearly as thick in places as the total depth of the sea outside. This may be 10,000 feet or more. We shall in fact have accounted in this way for coral reefs rising from great depths where the conditions for life would prevent them from ever getting a start.

It is no wonder this simple theory was received with great enthusiasm by very many famous scientists. In one of the best of the earlier summaries of the problem of coral reefs, the American scientist W. M. Davis said: 'Of all the coral reef theories Darwin's seems to me to be the best argued, in spite of his youth'.

I cannot tell of all the rival explanations which have been

put forward since the time of Darwin, for theorists have run riot, and many of the explanations have been good too, because their inventors have had much information about coral growth which was unknown to Darwin. The fundamental belief of all the rivals of Darwin is, however, that subsidence of the sea bottom has *not* taken place, and has *not been needed*. Some experts did not like the idea that vast areas of the Pacific Ocean floor had been sinking. But all these rivals had to explain how the coral grew up, or appeared to grow up from great depths.

You will remember that Chamisso thought simply of his coral atolls as growing outwards. The theory of Sir John Murray, the first great opponent of Darwin, urged this, too. He, however, definitely claimed that in the beginning a mass of coral commenced to grow upwards *on some shallow bank*. Its original shape would naturally depend on that of the shallow in the ocean, which might be a round shoal or an elongated one. Let us suppose that the original coral mass was circular in form. This coral mass would, said Murray, eventually reach the surface of the sea, a condition which would put an end to any more upward growth of coral, because the latter had reached the air and further upward growth was obviously impossible. However, there would be no reason why the coral on the outside (especially near the surface) could not continue growing. If we suppose that for hundreds of thousands of years the coral flourished greatly on the outside, but died on top after reaching the surface of the sea, then of course a ring of coral would gradually be formed. The lagoon would come where the coral died and decayed. We should have an atoll which would gradually grow bigger. But, you will probably say, how could the coral grow on the sloping and deeper sea bottom round the outside of the small atoll to make it bigger? Would not the sea there be too deep for the foundations? Sir John Murray's answer was clever. He claimed that the flourishing coral near the ocean

159

surface on the outside 'wall' of the reef would constantly suffer during storms, that the wild ocean surf would break away great boulders of the living coral, which would fall to the bottom of the sea and die and heap themselves up to make a new platform which in time would be high enough for coral to grow on it. And so the atoll (or a barrier reef) *would grow outwards on its own debris.*

This theory, like that of Darwin, could also be applied to explain the position of the outer reefs of our Great Barrier Reef area. It certainly makes it more difficult to find practical proof of the changes which must have taken place in the formation of such coral reefs.

Other theories have been invented to try to explain the origin of the Great Barrier Reef, and many specialists consider that it is exceptionally difficult to be sure of its history. We shall show in a moment, however, that recently scientists have again collected evidence to support the theory of Darwin, and with the latest discoveries in other parts of the world, this old theory of a subsiding sea bottom is today very much in favour.

And now to sum this up, it must be understood that if Darwin's theory is correct, and there is a subsiding sea bottom in any barrier reef or atoll region, then the original and ancient sea bottom which was once shallow water must now lie at a considerable depth and there should be a great thickness of coral on top of it. On the other hand, if Murray's theory is true, it means that an atoll or a barrier reef is somewhere a relatively thin veneer of coral on top of some shallow part of the sea. There may be thick coral in places where it has fallen and piled up on a slope. By and large, however, the original rock will not be so deep down. This fact gave our scientific detectives the best clue to a practicable method for discovering whether Darwin's fascinating idea about the origin of the atolls or barrier reef was correct. Why not bore holes down through a coral island and find the thickness of the coral reef material and the actual depth of the original sea bottom where the coral commenced to grow?

The Royal Society of England was first with a plan and the necessary finance. The atoll of Funafuti in the south Pacific was chosen as a suitable example. The expedition which left for Funafuti in 1899 became an adventure in itself, and one in which Australia eventually played a big part because of the close association with Sydney University. The successful completion of the boring was carried out under the guidance of the late Sir Edgeworth David, then Professor of Geology at Sydney. But the result, although the bore hole was sunk through 1,114 feet of coral reef material and thus supported Darwin, was asserted to be unconvincing. The supporters of Murray's view claimed that the bore might by chance have gone through a place where coral fragments had rolled or drifted down the side of a submarine mountain and had become piled up! This was a shock for the Darwinists. What arguments were to be heard in the science lecture rooms of Burlington House, Piccadilly, London! These were heydays for marine biologists. But money for further boring was not forthcoming.

Some years went by and then in 1918 the Japanese tried a new and different method which did not entail boring, on Jaluit Island in the Marshalls. Again the result showed that a considerable thickness of limestone was present, but this time the figures were criticized because of a certain vagueness about them, and the method was new and uncertain.

Now, sinking bore holes through coral reefs is an expensive game—especially for scientists who are not likely thereby to cash in on finds of rare minerals, but are only to get an answer to their curiosity. Yet such was this curiosity that Australia was again drawn in, and, after a few years (1928) a bore was sunk on one of our own reefs, on Michaelmas Cay about ten miles inside the outer barrier of the Great Barrier Reef (and about 22 miles N.N.E. of Cairns). This bore passed through no less than 427 feet of coralline material. (The reader will remember that reef coral does not flourish below 150–180 feet.) This was not all, however, for the bore was continued as far as 600 feet and still no definite basic ancient rock platform was reached.

The material of the bore was, however, something of a puzzle. The late Professor Richards, of the University of Queensland, stated that no one who examined the bore material 'could pretend that the coralline material has been formed *in situ* as far as growth position is concerned. . . . It would appear as if the "factory" was somewhere else, and the disruption fragments had accumulated on the leeward side as it were'. Notwithstanding the nature of the materials Richards added that whether the coralline material was *in situ* or not, *the fact that subsidence of 600 feet* had taken place appeared to be 'inescapable'. So we have another piece of evidence for the old Darwinian theory.

The Queensland geologists did not stop at this, and in 1937 they made still another experiment. This time they sank a bore on the popular tourist resort, Heron Island, which, as we have seen, occupies quite a different and interesting position in the reef area. Surmounting the many difficulties once more, for coral material is not easy for boring experiments, a total depth of 732 feet was reached without meeting anything but limy material. In view of the distance apart of Michaelmas Cay and Heron Island, and the different relations to the land and the outer barrier, Professor Richards in summing up the result had to say that 'the remarkable similarity in the bores as to thickness and physical make-up of the coralline material was difficult to think of as just coincidence'. In other words, he again had to conclude from evidence obtained in the Great Barrier Reef region that subsidence of considerable amount had taken place, and that Darwin's theory was once more favoured by the results.

This has brought us to the latest and most surprising adventure of all. Who on earth would have expected that the invention and use of the atomic bomb might do anything towards solving this problem of the origin of barrier reefs and atolls? Yet it has done so.

When World War II was over, the United States authorities decided, and quite naturally, to find out exactly what an atomic bomb might do if exploded in different sorts of situations, and they had never exploded one over the sea and ships. They concluded that a lonely atoll in the Pacific was the best possible spot for a marine test, and so chose Bikini Atoll. Having removed the small native population the U.S. staff proceeded to work in a manner which, despite my hatred of war, captured my appreciation. They made the most complete scientific investigation of the atoll and its lagoon that was possible, even sending zoologists to make detailed collections of the sea life.

Science in combination with commerce has, however, discovered new methods which are used particularly in finding minerals and rocks with petroleum, for studying what lies below the earth's surface. The old costly method of boring is of course definite and will be required in any case, but a new practice called seismic sounding has been invented which is most valuable as a preliminary, and the U.S. engineers are particularly good at this work by reason of their interest in oil deposits. The method uses little explosions, and the time taken for transmission of the explosion waves through the ground gives information about the depth and nature of different beds of rock. Sound travels at different speeds through various types of rock and these speeds are known.

Five bore holes were sunk on Bikini Island and in addition no fewer than 126 of the seismic shots were made. The depth of material above the ancient basement rock in the centre of the lagoon (and likely to be limy material) was actually discovered by the seismic method to be probably about 7,000 feet. The borings themselves were carried down as far as 2,556 feet without meeting any basement rock (as would be expected from the seismic results). The material of the bores—rather loose limy stuff except for a layer of 'fairly firm limestone' at 1,100–1,135 feet—could with our modern knowledge even be dated, and it is claimed that some layers of rock within the depths studied must have been formed twenty or thirty million years ago (Miocene Age, as the geologists put it). All the results supported the theory that the bottom of the ocean has subsided. So once again the old Darwinian explanation of atolls and barrier reefs was sustained. This is surely more than coincidence.*

I have told this remarkable story because I really believe that those who visit the reefs of the outer barrier of the Great Barrier Reef, and Heron Island, and others nearer the mainland, must be interested to know how the 'land' on which they enjoy themselves comes to be there. They should know how, for long ages, the coral has grown upwards whilst the sea bottom has subsided, one keeping pace with the other.

We end this story with the reminder that some corals in the Great Barrier Reef lagoons, growing in a few feet of shallow water, may be only a few years old—the simple consequence of the larvae of coral animals having drifted about in the surface waters until they reached suitable firm objects to which they might attach themselves. But the reefs of the mighty outer barrier, like the great barrier reef along the coast of New Caledonia, and hundreds of other beautiful coral islets which rise from very deep ocean water, are the consequence of the growth of live things, the movements of

---

*In the decade since this book was first published considerably more work has been carried out on the coral reefs of both the Pacific and the Atlantic oceans. On Eniwetok Atoll in the Marshall Group the drills went beyond 4,000 feet. The work is discussed in a paper by H. S. Ladd published in the journal *Science* for September 1961.

the earth's crust, and intervention of the elements (weather, tides, etc.), for possibly millions of years.

It must be emphasized that this is the story of a great scientific effort to explain the origin of certain of the earth's most remarkable scenery. The effort is not by any means finished. Indeed we should be foolish to expect that all coral reefs and islands had passed through the same stages. At this point we can only say that it is surprising that at such different places as Funafuti, Jaluit Island, Michaelmas Cay, Heron Island, and Bikini and Eniwetok atolls, the real practical evidence has all pointed to the earth's surface having undergone subsidence and that Darwin's theory, which demands subsidence, is the explanation of coral reefs.

Yet in the Pelsart Group of our own Western Australian coral archipelago of the Abrolhos, we have something which looks exactly like an atoll, but is not a true atoll, and probably if the story of the past events leading to the present Abrolhos Islands could only be revealed, it would be anything but a simple story. One is always inclined to forget the word simplicity when viewing nature's work. One thing at least is clear when we marvel at the beauties of a coral reef, which arises abruptly from the ocean's depths and withstands the ocean's swell better than any man-made concrete breakwater, and that is the persistence of Life. There are singularly few places on the earth's surface from the dark abysses of the sea, to the tops of the highest mountains, from the coral flat to the desert, where life in some form does not hold its own and persist through the ages.

POSTSCRIPT TO THE CHAPTER

We have by no means dealt adequately with all the theories which have been suggested to explain the formation of coral reefs and islands. But that is not the intention of this book, and there are other books for the specialist. However, it is

165

quite possible (in view of the explanations of the estuaries of Sydney and the Hawkesbury River in semi-popular works) that some reader may have heard of the theories of an American scientist named Daly, and so a very brief summary is added of his contribution, which is called the Glacial Control Theory.

Once upon a time the earth's surface suffered great lowerings in temperature known as the glacial period. (Actually there were several glacial periods, but we are just concerned with the last one.) Now, Daly pointed out that when a glacial period caused a great thickening of the polar ice and an extension too of the ice round say the North Pole, sea water would be drawn away from other regions of the earth. He counted on a fall of at least 150 feet (sometimes it is put at 300 feet) in sea-level in the tropics.

One result of this might well be that shoals or submarine platforms which had been too deep for the growth of reef corals were brought to suitable depths. It would also probably cause new shallow platforms to originate. Daly assumed that reef corals would grow round the margins of these shallow platforms and that gradually as the ice age passed away the sea would return to the tropics and the sea-level would slowly and gradually rise, taking many years.

Such a gradual rise in sea-level, keeping pace with the growth of coral, would be practically the same as a slow subsidence of the sea bottom.

This theory of Daly's and other theories, as well as combinations of two of them, have not been discussed in greater detail because the discoveries made through boring, and especially the explorations at the Bikini Atoll, have turned the situation so much in favour of Darwin's old theory. They certainly favour subsidence of a far greater amount than the change in sea-level accounted for by Daly.

Readers must remember, however, that we still know too little about coral reefs to account for the whole process in the case of any particular atoll or barrier reef, and there is no doubt that different islands have been the result of different cycles of events.

The ocean still has its secrets for generations of future scientists, who are in the fortunate position of having not only the results of a century of laboriously gained knowledge to build on, but also the advantage of a great variety of new apparatus and technique, including the aqualung, the bathoscope, mass spectrometry and micro-palaeontology, and the use of radioactive isotopes and the electron miscroscope.

APPENDIX

THE GREAT BARRIER REEF
FOR THE TOURIST*

THE cooler months of the Australian year, April to September, are most suitable for visits to the resorts of the Great Barrier Reef, from Heron Island in the south to Green Island, 600 miles to the north. This is a time of cloudless bright, sunny days and cool, clear nights. The atmosphere is one of tropical informality. However, excellent conditions for reefing, swimming, fishing and cruising continue on from October until December. The visitor needs only fairly light clothing, with something warmer for night wear, and the only particular advice a tourist need take is to equip himself with sun-glasses and protective headwear and, for coral fossicking on the Reef, rubber-soled shoes or boots.

As the reader of this book is already aware, there are a great many islands stretched out along the 1,260 miles of the Reef, but the main resorts fall into three areas—northern, central and southern. They comprise Green, Dunk, Bedarra, Orpheus and Magnetic islands, off Cairns and Townsville in the north; the Whitsunday Passage group of Hayman, Lindeman, South Molle, Long and Brampton in the centre; and Heron and Quoin, off Gladstone in the south.

These reef resorts are reached by travelling north from Brisbane or Sydney by air, rail or road to various stepping-

---

*This appendix has been prepared by the Australian National Travel Association.

168

off points along the Queensland coast. Transport from the coast to the different islands is by launch or by air, the traveller sometimes having a choice between the two.

Taking the main resorts from north to south, the following gives an indication of the sort of facilities a visitor can enjoy and some indication of the sort of prices he can expect to pay for them. Tariffs and timetables are, of course, subject to change at short notice.

Green Island, 18 miles north-east of Cairns, is (as Professor Dakin has reminded the reader) one of the few resort islands which is itself actually a coral island. It is famous for its underwater observatory, where coral and incredibly colourful reef fish can be seen in their natural state. Aqualung air cylinders are available for skin divers, glass-bottom boats can be hired, and a cinema on the island shows films about the Barrier Reef. The whole 30-acre island is a national park where bird and surrounding marine life is protected. Access: By plane (daily), rail (six-day-a-week, air-conditioned service) or road from Sydney or Brisbane, then by launch (12s. 6d. return). Accommodation: This comprises older cabins sharing some central communal facilities and new single and twin self-contained units. The tariff, according to length of stay and location in old or new quarters, is from around £1 19s. per person per day to £2 10s.

Magnetic Island, largest of the resort islands, is five miles out from Townsville. Dominated by Mount Cook (1,682 feet), it has a number of perfect swimming beaches and facilities for fishing, bowling and golf. Organized barbecues are a feature of life on Magnetic. Access: Air, road or rail to Townsville, then by 40-minute launch which departs on Mondays and Fridays and leaves the island on Saturdays and Sundays. The launch fare is 5s. return. Accommodation: Because of its size, Magnetic offers a variety of licensed hotel, private hotel and guesthouse accommodation, much of it comprising individual cabins. Tariffs vary from £1 15s. at one of the guesthouses to £3 daily at the Hotel Magnetic.

Hayman Island, most northerly of the Whitsunday Group, offers first-class accommodation and facilities for swimming, fishing, water skiing, bowling, tennis, skin-diving and catamaran and outrigger-canoe sailing. Launches take visitors out to the Reef proper where they can fossick for coral. The fully licensed Royal Hayman Hotel, main centre on the 900-acre island, has a swimming pool, and entertainment includes barbecues, carnivals and cabaret evenings. Access: By air to Proserpine or Mackay, by rail or road to Mackay, then by road to nearby Cannonvale and on by launch (Tuesday, Friday and Sunday). Alternatively, visitors can travel by seaplane from Mackay. The 19-mile launch trip costs £3 return; the plane fare from Mackay is £6 10s. each way. Accommodation: Tariffs vary from £5 per person per day to £2 12s. 6d.

South Molle Island, a few miles south of Hayman, is noted for the brightness and informality of its resort life. The 1,040-acre island offers an unusual variety of scenery, from rugged heights to secluded bays. The tariff at the licensed resort includes free cruises, with additional charges for speed-boat and fishing trips. Attractions include swimming, fishing, coral viewing, tennis and aquaplaning. Access: By launch (Tuesdays, Fridays and Sundays) from Cannonvale —£1 10s. return. Accommodation: Tariffs for cabins, suites and bungalows vary from £3 to £4 5s. per person per day.

Lindeman Island, almost completely surrounded by coral reefs, is 42 miles out from Mackay at the southern entrance to the Whitsunday Passage. Attractions include a swimming pool, catamaran sailing, coral viewing, aquaplaning, skin-diving, fishing and cruising. The island is licensed, and entertainment includes dances, movies, and moonlight cruises. Access: By plane from Mackay (the island has its own airport). The fare for the 20-minute flight is £10 5s. return and the service operates from Mackay on Friday, Saturday, Sunday and Tuesday. Accommodation: The tariff, which includes cruising, coral viewing, catamaran

sailing and morning and afternoon refreshments, is £4 8s.
per person per day.

Heron Island, like Green Island, is a true coral island.
Only half a mile long and a quarter of a mile wide, it is 45
miles out from Gladstone. The island and surrounding reef
are protected, but spearfishing is provided for at Wistari
Reef, ten minutes by launch from Heron. The island is
noted for its birdlife and turtles. Special facilities are available for skindiving, including a compressor for recharging
aqualung air tanks. There is water skiing on the island's
protected lagoon and visitors can fossick on the exposed
reef at low tide. ACCESS: By air, rail or road to Gladstone
and then 45 miles out by launch. The launch fare is £4
return. ACCOMMODATION: The tariff for the older bungalows
and a new block varies from £3 3s. to £4 8s. per person per
day. *N.B.*—Because of its distance from the mainland and
the unavailability of a doctor, children under five years are
not accommodated.

These are only some of the main resorts. Others include
the fully licensed Brampton Island in the Whitsunday Group;
the quieter, 'away from it all', Orpheus Island, 50 miles out
from Townsville; and Quoin Island, close into Gladstone,
with its swimming pool, new accommodation units and
attractive tropical flowering trees.

An attractive alternative to staying at any one resort is to
embark on a cruise vessel calling in at a number of the better-
known islands. The Roylen Cruises from Mackay and the
Esmeralda Cruises from Cannonvale take up to 25 passengers on five-day trips taking in Long, Hayman, Lindeman,
South Molle and Brampton, where they stop for swimming
and to give passengers a taste of the different sorts of resort
life available. These licensed cruises also make stops for
fishing and coral fossicking. The charge is £29 10s. per
person.

Reef waters are something of a paradise for fishermen,
with groper, marlin, Spanish mackerel, tuna, barracouta,

red emperor and many other species plentiful. The abundance of fish, the clearness of the water and the beauty of the coral make the whole area particularly attractive for skindivers. Swimmers and skindivers, however, are warned not to disregard the shark danger. Visitors can take their own fishing equipment with them and all necessary tackle is available on the islands.

The climate makes the Reef a happy hunting ground for photographers. However, the very perfection of the climate, with its bright blue skies, means that the light is very intense, and photographers should not be misled by their light-meters into over-exposing film. They are also advised to use haze or sky light filters to avoid an over-blue effect in colour pictures. Cameras should be kept out of the sun as much as possible to prevent film deterioration, and, once removed from the camera, film should be kept well away from the light.

INDEX

Index

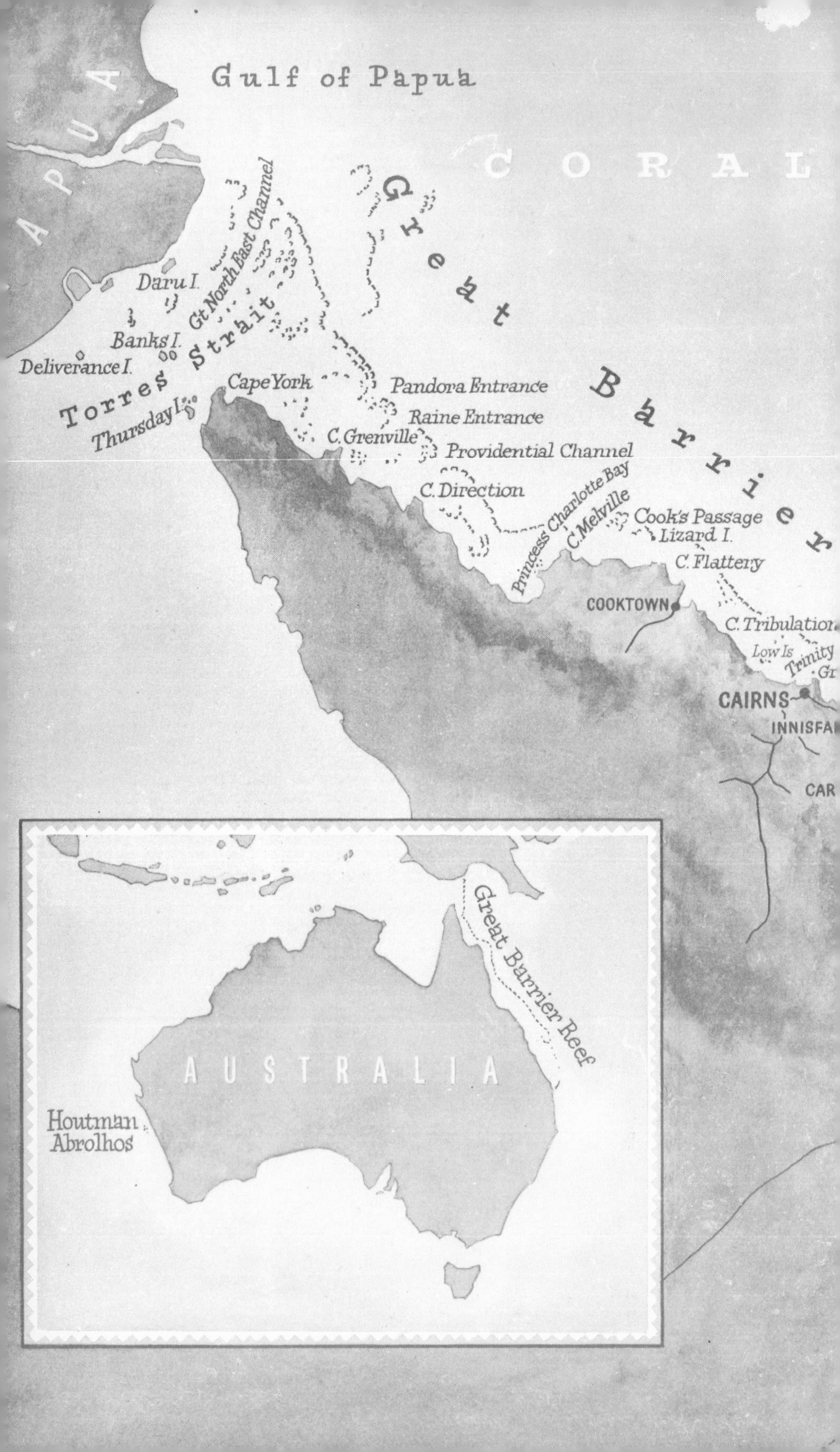

Gulf of Papua

C O R A L

P A P U A

Great

Barrier

Daru I.

Gt North East Channel

Banks I.

Deliverance I.

Thursday I.

Torres Strait

Cape York

Pandora Entrance

Raine Entrance

C. Grenville

Providential Channel

C. Direction

Princess Charlotte Bay

C. Melville

Cook's Passage

Lizard I.

C. Flattery

COOKTOWN

C. Tribulation

Low Is.

Trinity

Gr

CAIRNS

INNISFA

CAR

AUSTRALIA

Great Barrier Reef

Houtman
Abrolhos